Course

Chemistry Fundamentals II Lab

Course Number **CHM2046L**

Univ Of Central Florida

CHEMISTRY

http://create.mheducation.com

ISBN-10: 1307191797   ISBN-13: 9781307191790

Contents

i. Introduction to Student   1

1. Electrolytes in Solution: Completing the Circuit   2

2. Measurement and Proper Use of Laboratory Glassware   12

3. Gas Stoichiometry: The Automobile Airbag   24

4. Limiting Reactants: How Much BaSO4 Can We Make?   33

5. Colligative Properties: Analysis of Freezing Point Depression   42

6. Antacid Analysis and the Determination of the Percent Acetic Acid in Vinegar   52

7. Introduction to Kinetics: Factors That Affect the Rate of Reaction   66

8. Determining the Rate Law: A Kinetics Study of the Iodination of Acetone   79

9. Spectrophotometric Analysis: Phosphates in Water   87

10. Thermochemistry   96

11. A Titration for the Determination of Ions in Water: The Hard Truth   110

Credits

i. Introduction to Student: *Instructor submitted material* 1

1. Electrolytes in Solution: Completing the Circuit: *Chapter 9 from Hands-On Chemistry Laboratory Manual by Paradis, 2006* 2

2. Measurement and Proper Use of Laboratory Glassware: *Chapter 5 from Hands-On Chemistry Laboratory Manual by Paradis, 2006* 12

3. Gas Stoichiometry: The Automobile Airbag: *Chapter 16 from Hands-On Chemistry Laboratory Manual by Paradis, 2006* 24

4. Limiting Reactants: How Much BaSO4 Can We Make?: *Chapter 8 from Hands-On Chemistry Laboratory Manual by Paradis, 2006* 33

5. Colligative Properties: Analysis of Freezing Point Depression: *Chapter 22 from Hands-On Chemistry Laboratory Manual by Paradis, 2006* 42

6. Antacid Analysis and the Determination of the Percent Acetic Acid in Vinegar: *Chapter 15 from General Chemistry Laboratory Manual by Van Koppen, 2003* 52

7. Introduction to Kinetics: Factors That Affect the Rate of Reaction: *Chapter 23 from Hands-On Chemistry Laboratory Manual by Paradis, 2006* 66

8. Determining the Rate Law: A Kinetics Study of the Iodination of Acetone: *Chapter 24 from Hands-On Chemistry Laboratory Manual by Paradis, 2006* 79

9. Spectrophotometric Analysis: Phosphates in Water: *Chapter 14 from Hands-On Chemistry Laboratory Manual by Paradis, 2006* 87

10. Thermochemistry: *Chapter 6 from General Chemistry Laboratory Manual by Van Koppen, 2003* 96

11. A Titration for the Determination of Ions in Water: The Hard Truth: *Chapter 13 from Hands-On Chemistry Laboratory Manual by Paradis, 2006* 110

Dear Student,

Welcome to general chemistry laboratory! Depending on your previous laboratory experiences, this course may be quite different than you expect. The entire semester is taught through a guided inquiry format intended to improve your critical thinking skills and advance your understanding of chemistry concepts. Each week, you will work with your classmates to develop unique experimental procedures in hopes of answering the key question. Whether your initial answer is right or wrong will not have an impact on your grade. What is important is that your claim is supported by your evidence and that you compare your claim to what other scientists have found. Due to the unique nature of the course, the use of the laboratory manual will also be unique. The manual will act mainly as a background source which you will read **after** experimentation.

To complement the guided inquiry nature of the experiments, the laboratory notebooks will be kept in the science writing heuristic SWH format. This format, as seen in the template below, will guide you through thought development in the form of writing. Numerous research studies have shown that high implementation of the SWH results in significantly higher test scores. The benefits of this implementation have been documented to last all year with the greatest student gain occurring within the first semester (Poock, Burke, Greenbowe, and Hand, 2003; Burke, Poock, Greenbowe and Hand, 2004).

The Science Writing Heuristic: Template for students

1. **Beginning ideas**- What were the beginning ideas?
2. **Tests**- What was done?
3. **Observations**- What happened?
4. **Evidence**- What is the evidence to make this claim?
5. **Claims**- What claim can be made?
6. **Reading**- How do the ideas developed in the lab compare with other scientists' ideas?
7. **Reflection**- How have my ideas changed?
8. **Writing**- What is the best explanation that clarifies what was learned?

The template for the SWH student template adapted from Greenbowe, Hand, 2005

We are excited to have you in the class and we wish you the best of luck. If you work hard in lab and study even harder at home, you will be surprised to discover how good of a chemist you already are!

Electrolytes in Solution: Completing the Circuit

Kristen Spotz

OBJECTIVES

- Understand how various compounds behave when dissolved in water.
- Develop a method for categorizing compounds based on the ability of their aqueous solutions to conduct electricity.
- Practice naming some common compounds.

INTRODUCTION

Imagine taking a walk along the seashore on a clear sunny day. As you enter the water, you think about the chemistry you have learned. You know that the oceans of our world are far from being pure H_2O. They are, in fact, aqueous solutions composed of countless substances dissolved in the water. Do these dissolved substances exist in solution as neutral molecules or as charged ions having the capacity to conduct an electrical current? What if the sky suddenly darkened and a bolt of lightening struck directly above you? (Figure 1) Are you safe, or have you just become part of a gigantic electrical circuit?

Figure 1. A bolt of lightening crashes off shore

BACKGROUND

Water and Solubility

Water is a remarkable solvent. Aqueous solutions can be made by dissolving in water many different compounds, both ionic and covalent/molecular. The oceans and lakes around us, as well as our very cells, are all examples of aqueous solutions.

As you might expect, not all things dissolve in water to the same extent. Scientists quantify the extent to which a particular solute dissolves in water by determining the solubility of the solute at a given temperature (typically, grams of solute per liter of water). For example, $NaCl$ is very soluble in water. At 20°C, one liter of water can accommodate 365 g of $NaCl$ before becoming <u>saturated</u>. Other compounds, such as $CaSO_4$, are labeled as insoluble meaning that less than 1 g of the material will dissolve in one liter of water. Insoluble compounds require very little solute before becoming saturated.

It is important to note that although textbooks give solubility rules describing compounds as either strictly soluble or insoluble, in actuality, solubility covers a whole spectrum. Even soluble compounds have their limits. Once the solubility of a compound is reached, no more will dissolve. For example, if you attempt to add more than 365 grams of $NaCl$ to 1 liter of water at 20°C, the excess will sit on the bottom in the form of an undissolved solid. On the opposite end of the spectrum, even "insoluble" compounds can dissolve to a very small extent.

Physical Properties of Aqueous Solutions

Depending on the nature of the dissolved solute (ionic or covalent/molecular), the solute may be present in solution in the form of ions or as neutral molecules. All soluble ionic compounds (this includes the strong bases) exist as ions in solution. For example, when dissolved in water, $NaCl$ exists as Na^+ and Cl^- ions (Figure 2). Even in the case of slightly soluble ionic compounds, where the majority of the solute is left undissolved on the bottom, all of the compound that did dissolve is in the form of ions. Although Figure 2 serves as an adequate representation of the behavior of soluble ionic compounds in water, a more realistic drawing is presented in Figure 3, where the dissolved ions are shown to be <u>hydrated</u>.

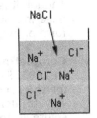

Figure 2. The behavior of ionic compounds (aq).

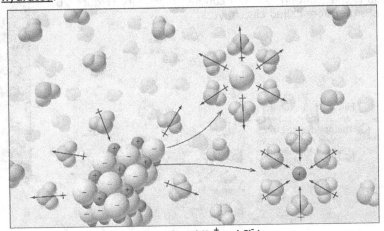

Figure 3. Hydrated Na^+ and Cl^- ions.

If, however, the solute placed in water is covalent/molecular, then the behavior of the solute is more complicated. Sometimes the solution will consist of neutral molecules as is the case with O_2 (Figure 4). Other covalent compounds break apart in solution to create varying amounts of ions. Let's take a closer look at this last category of compounds.

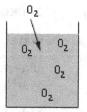

Figure 4. The behavior of nonelectrolytes (aq)

Strong and weak acids along with weak bases are a small, but important group of molecules that ionize in water. The degree of ionization depends on the strength of the acid or base. For example, strong acids, such as HCl, ionize nearly 100% in water to produce H^+ and Cl^- ions (Figure 5). However, with weak acids and weak bases, such as HF or NH_3 only a small fraction (less than 5%) of the molecules ionize leaving the majority of the solute molecules intact (Figure 6).

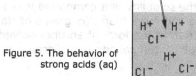

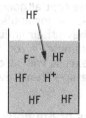

Figure 5. The behavior of strong acids (aq)

Figure 6. The behavior of weak acids and bases (aq)

Though it is not crucial to this discussion, you may be aware that free H^+ ions don't actually exist in solution. It is more realistic to represent them as bonded to a water molecule in the form of <u>hydronium ions</u>.

Completing the Circuit

In 1883, Svante Arrhenius proposed that ions are responsible for the conductivity of electricity through a solution. So, one way to identify the form (ionic or covalent) of the dissolved solute is to test the electrical conductivity of the particular aqueous solution (Figure 7a). Because the flow of electricity requires the presence of mobile charged particles, aqueous solutions that contain ions will conduct electricity (Figure 7b) and are therefore called electrolytes.

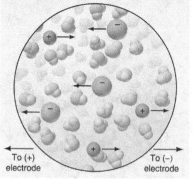

Figure 7b. In solution, anions move towards the positive electrode and cations move towards the negative electrode.

To (+) electrode   To (−) electrode

Figure 7a. Conductivity apparatus

The extent to which a particular solution conducts an electrical current depends on what proportion of solute particles dissociate into ions (Figure 8). Compounds whose solutions contain a large fraction of the solute in the form of ions (all soluble ionic compounds or strong acids) will conduct a large current and are called strong electrolytes. By contrast, a weak electrolyte is a solution that contains only a relatively small fraction of ionized solute particles (the weak acids and weak bases). As a result, solutions of weak electrolytes only conduct a small amount of current. Finally, a solution of a non-electrolyte, for example CO_2, contains only dissolved molecules and will not conduct an electrical current.

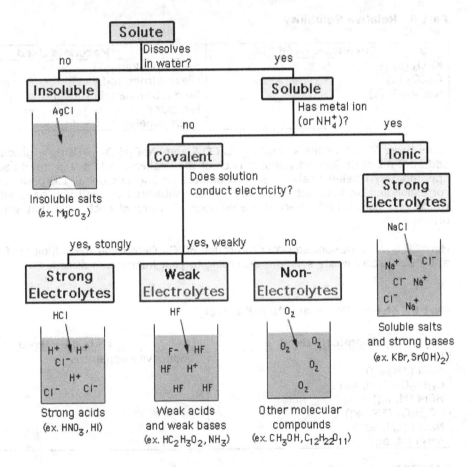

Figure 8. Flowchart for determining whether a compound is a strong, weak, or non-electrolyte.

OVERVIEW

In this experiment, you will determine the relative solubility of several ionic compounds by adding the compound to water in small portions until no more dissolves. You will also use a conductivity apparatus (Figure 7a) to test the conductivity of several solutions.

PROCEDURE

Part A. Relative Solubility

Chemicals Used	Materials Used
KNO_3 (s) $CaCO_3$ (s) $NaC_2H_3O_2$ (s)	50 mL Beakers (3) Glass stirring rod 50 mL Graduated cylinder Hot plate Thermometer

Label three 50-mL beakers "KNO_3", "$CaCO_3$" and "$NaC_2H_3O_2$". Using a graduated cylinder, add 20.0 mL of de-ionized water to each of the beakers. Add 1.0 gram of each solid to the appropriately labeled beaker. Stir. Continue adding additional 1.0-gram portions to the corresponding beakers until the solutions are saturated or until you have added 5 grams, which ever comes first. Record the number of grams of each solid that you were able to dissolve.

Heat 20.0 mL of de-ionized water to around 60°C. Determine the solubility of KNO_3 in water at 60°C. Discard waste solutions according to your instructor's directions.

Part B. Strong, Weak and Non-Electrolytes

Chemicals Used	Materials Used
NaCl (s) NaCl (1M, aq) $C_{12}H_{22}O_{11}$ (1M, aq) HCl (1M, aq) $HC_2H_3O_2$ (1M, aq) NaOH (1M, aq) NH_3 (1M, aq)	Conductivity apparatus

CAUTION: Be careful to avoid an electric shock when working with the conductivity apparatus. Unplug the conductivity apparatus before rinsing the electrodes or putting the electrodes down.

Your instructor will have stations with labeled 100-mL beakers containing 50 mL of each of the chemicals listed above. Test the conductivity of each sample and record the relative brightness of the light using the following scale: bright, dim, faint or no light. Be sure to rinse the electrodes before testing each solution.

Part C. Effect of Concentration on Conductivity

Chemicals Used	Materials Used
2 M HCl	100-mL beaker 50-mL Graduated cylinder Plastic pipet Conductivity apparatus

Using the graduated cylinder, transfer 50.0 mL of de-ionized water to a 100-mL beaker. Add 2 M hydrochloric acid drop-wise (up to a maximum of 50 drops) to the de-ionized water. Stir the solution and observe the conductivity after each drop of hydrochloric acid is added. Record the number of drops at which you first notice the light and again when the light is bright. Discard waste solutions according to your instructor's directions.

Part D. Conductivity of Household Substances

Chemicals Used	Materials Used
Epsom salt ($MgSO_4$) Rubbing alcohol (C_3H_7OH) Baking soda ($NaHCO_3$) Vinegar ($HC_2H_3O_2$)	100-mL Beakers (4) 50-mL Graduated cylinder Stirring rod Conductivity apparatus

Your instructor will have stations with labeled 100-mL beakers containing 50 mL of each of the household chemicals listed above. Test the conductivity of each sample and record the relative brightness of the light using the following scale: bright, dim, faint or no light. Be sure to rinse the electrodes before testing each solution.

Electrolytes in Solution: Completing the Circuit

Name:	Lab Instructor:
Date:	Lab Section:

PRE-LABORATORY EXCERCISES

1. Define the <u>underlined</u> words in the BACKGROUND section.

2. In this laboratory experiment, you will be studying the solubility of KNO_3, $CaCO_3$, and $NaC_2H_3O_2$ in water. Use the solubility rules in your textbook to make predictions about whether each compound is expected to be soluble or insoluble in water.

3. Which sample of water (seawater, tap water or de-ionized water) do you think will be the best conductor of electricity? The poorest conductor? Explain.

4. Why is it important to use de-ionized water when preparing the aqueous solutions in this experiment?

OVER →

PRE-LABORATORY EXERCISES continued...

5. For each compound (calcium chloride, glucose and sodium iodide) give the formula, state whether it is ionic or covalent, whether it is soluble in water, whether it forms ions in water, and whether an aqueous solution conducts electricity. Also make a drawing illustrating the behavior of the compound in water. Use Figure 8 to help you make your predictions. Use the space below to arrange your answers in the form of a table.

Electrolytes in Solution: Completing the Circuit

Name:	Lab Instructor:
Date:	Lab Section:

RESULTS and POST-LABORATORY QUESTIONS

Part A. Relative Solubility

Compound	Name	Grams Dissolved (room temp. water)	Grams Dissolved (warm water)
KNO_3			
$CaCO_3$			
$NaC_2H_3O_2$			

Use your data from Part A to calculate the solubility of each of the compounds in room temperature water. Report the solubility in both grams/mL and molarity.

Which of the compounds would you describe as very soluble? Slightly soluble? Insoluble? How do your results compare to those predicted from the solubility rules listed in your text (see PRE-LABORATORY EXERCISE #2)?

What effect did the warm water have on the solubility of the KNO_3? Can you think of a practical example of this behavior?

Part B. Strong, Weak and Non-Electrolytes

Compound	Name	Relative Brightness	Strong, Weak or Non-Electrolyte
NaCl (s)			
NaCl (aq)			
$C_{12}H_{22}O_{11}$ (aq)	sucrose		
HCl (aq)			
$HC_2H_3O_2$ (aq)			
NaOH (aq)			
NH_3 (aq)			

Referring to Part B, why did the bulb light up when placed in an aqueous solution of sodium chloride, but not in solid sodium chloride?

OVER →

RESULTS and POST-LABORATORY QUESTIONS continued...

Part C. Effect of Concentration on Conductivity
From Part C, how many drops of HCl were added before you first noticed a light?   How many drops before the light became bright?

Based on your results, if you placed one gram of a soluble ionic compound (ex: NaCl) in a full-size swimming pool filled with de-ionized water, would you expect the solution to conduct an electrical current? Explain.

Part D. Conductivity of Household Substances

Compound	Name	Relative Brightness	Strong, Weak or Non-Electrolyte
$MgSO_4$ (aq)			
C_3H_7OH (aq)	propanol		
$NaHCO_3$ (aq)			
$HC_2H_3O_2$ (aq)			

In Parts B and D, you determined whether $NaOH$, NH_3, C_3H_7OH and $NaHCO_3$ are strong, weak or non-electrolytes. Based on your results, draw beakers showing atomic scale representations of aqueous solutions of these compounds. Use the drawings in Figure 8 as examples.

Measurement and Proper Use of Laboratory Glassware

David Roberts

OBJECTIVES

- Correctly use the terms: accuracy, precision and percent error.
- Identify and use the appropriate number of significant figures in measurements and calculations.
- Properly use select laboratory glassware and the analytical balance.
- Calibrate some commonly used glassware.

INTRODUCTION

Your success in science, especially chemistry, will depend on your ability to make measurements that are accurate and consistent. Reliable measurements, beginning with Antoine Laurent Lavoisier, the father of analytical chemistry, have led to our understanding of combustion, chemical composition, and a host of other discoveries. Whether your goal is to make important scientific discoveries, or to just pass this chemistry laboratory, your ability to make careful measurements is an invaluable tool. A big part of making careful scientific measurements involves understanding the limitations of the glassware used to carry out chemical experiments (Figure 1).

Figure 1. Assorted laboratory glassware.

BACKGROUND

Precision and Accuracy

Making quantitative observations or measurements is fundamental to all of science. With any measurement, there are always two factors to consider: accuracy and precision. Accuracy is a measure of how close a measurement is to the actual or theoretical value. Precision is a measure of how close a series of measurements are to one another. These terms are illustrated conceptually in the archer's target (Figure 2). In Figure 2, the target on the left shows an archer who is precise; the arrows are reproducibly clustered around a certain point, but the archer is not accurate because the arrows are not on the bull's eye. If you look at the middle target you will see that the archer was neither accurate nor precise. The arrows are scattered around the target. In the right-hand target, the archer was both accurate and precise. The archer was able to reproduce the same result and able to obtain the desired target.

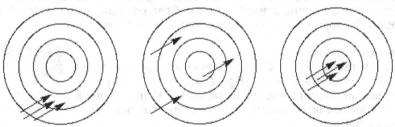

Figure 2. The use of arrows and targets to represent accuracy and precision.

Figure 2 also serves to illustrate the concepts of systematic (or determinate) error and random (or indeterminate) error. The target on the left is an example of systematic error where the archer keeps missing the target in the same fashion; maybe her sight is aligned incorrectly. This type of error can occur in the laboratory if, for example, a balance has been incorrectly calibrated and is adding 0.050 g to each measurement. The target in the middle is an example of random error. In the laboratory, this type of error occurs frequently as a result of sloppy or rushed work on the part of the scientist.

Percent Error

Scientists can evaluate the accuracy of a measurement by comparing the experimental value with the theoretical value. Suppose you measure the mass of a beaker using an analytical balance and the balance reads 283.25 grams. However, the theoretical value for the mass of the beaker is actually 285.00 grams. This difference between the theoretical value and the experimental value is called the error (Equation 1). Error can be either positive or negative depending on whether the experimental value is greater or less than the theoretical value.

$$\text{Error = Theoretical value - Experimental value} \qquad \text{Equation 1}$$

For our example, the error is 285.00 g – 283.25 g = +1.75 g. The absolute value of the error is used to calculate the percent error (or relative error) of the measurement (Equation 2).

$$\% \text{ Error} = \frac{|\text{Error}|}{\text{Theoretical value}} \times 100 \qquad \text{Equation 2}$$

For our example, $\% \text{ Error} = \dfrac{1.75 \text{ g}}{285.00 \text{ g}} \times 100 = 0.614 \%$

Significant Figures and Uncertainty in Measurements

Suppose you wanted to measure your weight using your bathroom scale that is calibrated in 1-pound intervals. On your bathroom scale you could easily read your weight to the nearest pound. In addition, you could also estimate your weight to the nearest tenth of a pound. Suppose you estimate your weight to be between 184 and 185 lbs; let's say 184.5 lbs. The first three digits are known with certainty, but the rightmost digit has been estimated and involves some uncertainty. Scientists often report numbers with plus or minus ranges indicating how uncertain the last digit is. For example, if we thought our weight might be between 184.3 and 184.7 lbs., we could report the weight as 184.5 ± 0.2 lbs. This measurement would have four significant digits. Significant figures include all the digits that are certain, plus the last digit that is estimated. The number of significant figures is related to the certainty of the measurement.

In this experiment you will explore the inherent error in the design of various types of glassware that will affect your ability to obtain accurate measurements. As you will see, it is essential that you understand the limits of the equipment and utilize this information when choosing the appropriate laboratory equipment and glassware.

Laboratory Balance

In the laboratory, we obtain the mass of an object using an electronic analytical balance (Figure 3). Typical laboratory balances can measure masses to within 0.001 g. To guide you in your use of an electronic top-loading balance follow these guidelines:

Figure 3. An electronic balance

- The balance should be left on at all times during use.
- Always use the same balance when making repetitive measurements.
- Make certain that all materials are weighed at room temperature.
- Never weigh objects directly on the balance pan. Always use a container or weighing paper on the balance pan.
- Wait for a stable reading before recording the mass.
- When finished, remove your container or weighing paper and clean up any spills.
- You may need to *tare* your container. To do so, press the tare button and wait until the balance shows a stable zero reading. That sets the balance to weigh anything that is placed into the container, but it does not weigh the container itself.

Glassware

When conducting chemical experiments, you will invariably need to use a piece of glassware. The specific glassware you choose depends on the task you are completing. Do you need to obtain as close to 50.00 mL of water as possible? Do you need to pour roughly 3.4 mL of a solution? Do you need to take a solid and make a solution with a carefully known concentration? Or do you just need a container to hold waste?

Beakers, Flasks and Graduated cylinders (Holding Glassware)

Erlenmeyer flasks (Figure 4a) and beakers (Figure 4b) are designed for mixing, transporting, and reacting liquids, but not for accurate volume measurements. The volumes stamped on the sides Erlenmeyer flasks and beakers have considerable error.

Figure 4a. Erlenmeyer flask

Figure 4b. Beaker

The graduated cylinder (Figure 5a) is a fast and convenient way to dispense an approximate volume of liquid. If you examine the graduated cylinder in Figure 5b, you can see the letters "TD". When a piece of glassware is designated "to deliver" (TD), it has been calibrated to dispense a quantity of liquid knowing that some of the liquid will stay behind. When using graduated cylinders we also have to deal with the tendency of liquids to form a meniscus (Figure 5b). When measuring volumes, it is important to be at eye level with the meniscus and to read the volume marking at the bottom of the meniscus.

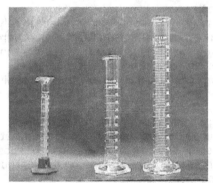

Figure 5a. Various graduated cylinders

Figure 5b. The meniscus

The Volumetric Pipet (Dispensing Glassware)

Volumetric pipets are another form of TD glassware, but unlike graduated cylinders, pipets are used to deliver accurate volumes of liquid. They come in a variety of sizes delivering fractions of a milliliter up to 100 ml or more. The pipet has one of the smallest margins of error for all dispensing glassware. For example, when a 5-ml pipet is used correctly it has been calibrated to deviate only ± 0.01 ml of the target volume. To ensure proper use of the pipet, it is crucial to adhere to the following guidelines:

- Clean the pipet with very dilute soapy water and rinse with de-ionized water.
- From the stock bottle transfer the solution you will pipet into a piece of holding glassware (ex. beaker or flask). Never put a pipet directly into a bottle of stock solution.
- Using a pipet bulb (Figure 6a), carefully fill the pipet with a small amount of the solution. Rotate the pipet so that the inside walls become coated with the solution. Discard the solution in the appropriate waste container.

- Fill the pipet with solution to a point above the calibration mark (be careful not to suck solution up into the bulb), remove the bulb and quickly cover the opening of the pipet with your index finger (Figure 6b).

Figure 6a.

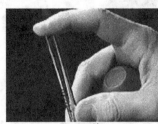
Figure 6b.

Figure 6c.

- Wipe the tip using a Kimwipe and allow the liquid to drain to the calibration mark. Be sure to read the meniscus at eye level (Figure 6c)

Figure 6d.

- Touch the tip of the filled pipet to the lower inside wall of receiving glassware and allow the pipet to drain completely (Figure 6d). As with any TD glassware, do not blow out the liquid remaining in the tip of the pipet.

Volumetric Flask (Containing Glassware)

Figure 7. A 500-mL volumetric flask.

Volumetric flasks are commonly used to accurately prepare a solution of known concentration. Unlike the glassware previously discussed, the volumetric flask is calibrated to contain (TC) a stated volume of liquid to four significant figures. To prepare solutions using a volumetric flask follow these guidelines:

- Clean and thoroughly rinse the flask.
- Always prepare solutions at room temperature.
- To dilute liquids: deliver a volume of concentrated liquid to the flask. Using a water bottle and a disposable pipet, carefully fill the flask to the calibration mark. Thoroughly mix by capping and inverting.
- To prepare solutions from solids: Completely dissolve the solid in a minimum amount of solvent. Using a water bottle and a disposable pipet, carefully fill the flask to the calibration mark. Thoroughly mix by capping and inverting.

Calculating Error and Percent Error of Select Glassware

In this laboratory exercise, the percent error of a piece of glassware will be assessed using the relationship between the mass and density of water. The error in any type of glassware is the difference between the actual volume delivered (based on the relationship between mass and density) and the theoretical volume (actual volume marking indicated on the glassware). Table 1 lists the density of water at various temperatures, which will aid you in completing this experiment.

Table 1. Density of water as a function of temperature

Temperature (°C)	Density of water (g/mL)	Temperature (°C)	Density of water (g/mL)
15	0.9991026	23	0.9975415
16	0.9989460	24	0.9972995
17	0.9987779	25	0.9970479
18	0.9985986	26	0.9967867
19	0.9984082	27	0.9965162
20	0.9982071	28	0.9962365
21	0.9979955	29	0.9959478
22	0.9977735	30	0.9956502

OVERVIEW

In this experiment you will practice proper laboratory techniques. You will then determine the accuracy of a 100-mL graduated cylinder, a 50-mL pipet and a 250-mL beakers by comparing your results to the rest of the class. Finally you will use a volumetric flask to make a solution of known concentration. The solution will then be diluted.

PROCEDURE

PART A. Performance Objectives

Materials used per pair	
50-mL Graduated cylinder	250-mL Beaker
50-mL Pipet and bulb	Top loading balance
100-mL Volumetric flask	Disposable pipet

Part A of this experiment is an opportunity for you to learn the proper procedure to "determine the mass of 50 mL of water transferred from a graduated cylinder to a beaker" and to "accurately deliver 50 mL of water to a volumetric flask". To obtain the most benefit from this exercise, review the information in the BACKGROUND pertaining to the handling of laboratory glassware. Then, practice performing the steps outlined in the following two "Tasks". Once you feel comfortable that you can perform the "Tasks" without the aid of your laboratory manual, give your manual to your laboratory partner and have them evaluate your work. For each step that you correctly perform, your partner will mark a √ in the corresponding column. After completing the task, evaluate your partner's performance.

Task A: Determine the mass of 50 mL of water transferred from a graduated cylinder to a beaker.

Performance objective	OK?
Clean graduated cylinder with diluted soapy water and rinse thoroughly.	
Carefully pour water into the cylinder until close to the desired volume.	
Reach final volume by using a disposable pipet to add water drop wise.	
Student reads the bottom of the meniscus at eye level to ensure accuracy.	
Place a clean, dry beaker on the balance pan.	
Wait for a stable reading and record the weight of the beaker.	
Leave the balance neat and clean.	
Transfer the water from the graduated cylinder into the beaker.	
Place the beaker with water onto the same balance used previously.	
Wait for a stable reading and record the weight.	
Leave the balance neat and clean.	

Task B: Accurately deliver 50 mL of water to a volumetric flask.

Performance objective	OK?
Clean and dry a beaker.	
Pour a volume of water, in excess of the desired amount (in this case, 50 mL) into the beaker.	
Clean the pipet with dilute, soapy water and rinse thoroughly.	
Rinse the pipet with the solution of interest (in this case, water).	
Draw the solution up past the calibration mark without sucking the solution into the bulb.	
Remove the bulb and quickly cap the pipet with an index finger.	
While at eye level with the pipet, slowly lower the solution to the calibration mark.	
Make sure the bottom of the meniscus is at the calibration mark.	
Touch the tip of the filled pipet with Kimwipe to remove excess solution.	
Lower the pipet inside the receiving glassware (in this case, a volumetric flask) and allow the pipet to completely drain.	
Do not blow out the last drop of solution on any "to deliver" (TD) glassware.	

PART B. Glassware Calibration

Materials Used per Individual	
100-mL Graduated cylinder	Analytical balance
50-mL Pipet and bulb	Thermometer
100-mL and 250-mL Beakers	

Weigh a clean, dry 100-mL beaker. Measure 50 mL of water using a 100-mL graduated cylinder. Carefully transfer the water from the graduated cylinder to the empty 100-mL beaker. Re-weigh the beaker. Record the temperature of the water in the beaker. Repeat this process two more times for the graduated cylinder.

Repeat the above process (three trials) using, first, a 50-mL pipet and then a 250-mL beaker in place of the graduated cylinder. Record your average experimental values for the volumes of water dispensed by each piece of glassware on the board with the class data. Be sure to record all of the class values in your notebook for later analysis.

PART C. Solution Preparation Using a Volumetric Flask

Chemicals Used	Materials Used
$Cu(SO_4) \cdot 5H_2O$ (s)	5-mL Pipet and bulb
	250-mL Beaker (1)
	100-mL Volumetric flask (2)

Weigh 0.500 g of $Cu(SO_4) \cdot 5H_2O$ (s) on a piece of weighing paper. Transfer the solid to a 100-mL volumetric flask.   Make Solution #1 by dissolving the solid and then diluting to the mark according to the steps described in the BACKGROUND for using a volumetric flask.

Next, prepare Solution #2 by pipeting 5.00 mL of the Solution #1 into a second 100-mL volumetric flask and diluting to the mark. Record your observations comparing Solution #1 to Solution #2.

Measurement and Proper Use of Laboratory Glassware

Name:	Lab Instructor:
Date:	Lab Section:

PRE-LABORATORY EXERCISES

1. Distinguish between the terms "mass" and "weight".

2. Using your textbook as a guide, summarize the rules for determining if a zero in a number is a significant figure. Give an example where a zero is significant and an example where it is not significant. For your two examples, also indicate how many significant figures are in each number.

3. Summarize the rules that apply to addition/subtraction operations and multiplication/division operations for significant figures.

4. Perform the following calculations. Include correct units and indicate the number of significant figures in each answer
    a) 1.456 m x 205 m

    b) 1.456 m + 205 m

OVER →

PRE-LABORATORY EXERCISES continued...

5. A student conducts three trials to determine the concentration of an unknown solution. She reports the following values: 0.210 M, 0.198 M and 0.203 M.   The actual concentration is 0.135 M.

    a) What is her average reported value?

    b) What is her error?

    c) What is her percent error?

    d) Was her work accurate? Was it precise? Explain.

    e) Did her work show systematic error? Did it show random error? Explain.

6. A small, empty container is found to weigh 2.356 g. The container is then filled with water (23°C). The full container is found to weigh 28.624 g. Using the information in Table 1 in the BACKGROUND, determine the volume of water (mL) in the beaker.

Measurement and Proper Use of Laboratory Glassware

Name:	Lab Instructor:
Date:	Lab Section:

RESULTS and POST-LABORATORY QUESTIONS

PART A. Performance Objectives
Are there any steps that you forgot to perform when your laboratory partner evaluated your ability to carry out Tasks A and B? If so, which steps?

PART B. Glassware Calibration
Attach copies of your data tables (one for each type of glassware tested). Your tables must include the following information for each of the three trials: Mass of empty glassware, mass of glassware and water, mass of water, temperature of water, corresponding density of water, volume of water, your experimental average, your error (compared to the average) and your percent error (again for the average and assuming a theoretical volume of 50.00 mL). Be careful to report all data with proper units and with the correct number of significant figures.

Beginning with the mass of the empty graduated cylinder, show all of your work for calculating the volume of water dispensed in Trial #1 with the graduated cylinder.

Beginning with the volumes of water dispensed by the graduated cylinder in the three trials, show all your work for calculating the average, the error (using the average) and the percent error (using the average experimental value) for the graduated cylinder.

What is the class average for the experimental volume of water dispensed by each piece of glassware. For each type of glassware, what is the class error (using the class average) and the class percent error. Based on these experimental results, which is the most accurate piece of glassware? Explain.

OVER →

RESULTS and POST-LABORATORY QUESTIONS continued...

PART B. Glassware Calibration continued...

For each piece of glassware indicate the range of class values (highest and lowest) for the experimental volume of water. Based on these experimental results, which is the most precise piece of glassware? Explain.

Which of the following pieces of glassware (volumetric flask, beaker, pipet or graduated cylinder) would be best suitable for the following tasks? Briefly explain each answer.

    a) Use as a waste container.

    b) To dilute a solution to a concentration with 4-significant figures.

    c) Accurately deliver 25.00 mL of solution.

    d) Quickly deliver approximately 25 mL of solution.

PART C. Solution Preparation using a Volumetric Flask

What is the concentration of Solution #1? Report your answer with the correct number of significant figures in terms of molarity (moles of $Cu(SO_4) \cdot 5H_2O$/liter of solution).

What did you observe by comparing Solution #1 to Solution #2? Does this make sense in terms of the relative concentrations? Explain.

Gas Stoichiometry: The Automobile Airbag

Joel Kelner

OBJECTIVE

- Design a model airbag as an example of a gas stoichiometry problem.
- Develop a laboratory protocol to solve a problem.
- Write a laboratory report.

INTRODUCTION

Since the late 1980's, thousands of lives have been saved by the collision protection provided by airbags (Figure 1). The death rate for drivers utilizing both seat belts and airbags is about 30% lower than the death rate among drivers using only seat belts.

Within 40 milliseconds after the initial automobile impact, the airbag is fully inflated, providing the crucial cushion between a possible life or death situation for the driver and passenger.

From the initial idea of airbags in 1953 to the modern state of airbags today has been a long journey with many obstacles for chemists and engineers. The development of a functional and safe airbag would not be possible without a firm understanding of chemical reactions and the behavior of gases.   Next time you ride in a car think about how the airbag is a prime example of science and technology ultimately benefiting mankind.

Figure 1. Deployment of an automobile airbag on a test dummy.

BACKGROUND

Airbags

The three chemicals stored in the gas generator of an airbag are sodium azide (NaN_3), potassium nitrate (KNO_3), and silicon dioxide (SiO_2). After a frontal impact of sufficient force, sensing devices located in the front of the car register the impact. The sensing devices send a signal to the generator, where a spark ignites the pellet of sodium azide causing a thermal decomposition (Equation 1). A pre-calculated volume of nitrogen gas is produced and fills the airbag almost completely to capacity (a little more N_2 gas is liberated in the second reaction). The other byproduct of the reaction is hazardous sodium metal, which poses a serious problem due to its reactivity with H_2O.

> **First Reaction**: Triggered by airbag sensor.

$$2NaN_3 \text{ (s)} \quad \rightarrow \quad 2Na \text{ (s)} \quad + \quad 3N_2 \text{ (g)} \qquad \qquad \text{Equation 1}$$

sodium azide   sodium metal   nitrogen gas

The scientists who developed the airbag had to devise a solution to this problem. They found that if potassium nitrate is added to the reaction the sodium can be transformed into a less harmful oxide. Combining the sodium metal with the potassium nitrate makes sense because one of the byproducts is more nitrogen gas (Equation 2).

> **Second Reaction**: Changes the sodium metal into oxides.

$$Na \text{ (s)} \quad + \quad KNO_3 \text{ (s)} \quad \rightarrow \quad K_2O \text{ (s)} \quad + \quad Na_2O \text{ (s)} \quad + \quad N_2 \text{ (g)} \qquad \text{Equation 2}$$

sodium metal   potassium nitrate   potassium oxide   sodium oxide   nitrogen gas

The final reaction deals with the remaining oxides. Realizing that the second reaction generates two oxides that could be used to produce a type of glass, the designers introduced silicon dioxide into the composition of airbags. This third reaction happens immediately after the second reaction and results in the formation of alkaline silicate glass (Equation 3). This step was instrumental in the marketing of airbags because there are no toxic materials remaining after deployment of the airbag. The alkaline silicate is very stable and will not ignite.

> **Third Reaction**: Changes the oxides into harmless glass.

$$K_2O(s) \quad + \quad Na_2O(s) \quad + \quad SiO_2 \rightarrow \text{alkaline silicate (glass)} \qquad \text{Equation 3}$$

potassium oxide   sodium oxide   silicon dioxide

Gas Stoichiometry

How does our discussion of air bags relate to gas stoichiometry? By knowing the airbag's desired volume, scientists can utilize gas stoichiometry to calculate the quantity of sodium azide required to fill the airbag to near capacity.

As with any problem involving gases, the ideal gas law ($PV=nRT$) will be important. In most gas stoichiometry problems, you are given information (mass, volume or moles) for one substance (A) and must make a conclusion about how much (mass, volume or moles) of another substance (B) can be produced. Take a moment to examine the following flow chart (Figure 2), which summarizes the typical steps in a gas stoichiometry problem. Each double-headed arrow represents one step in solving the problem. The actual number of steps in your calculation will depend on the initial known values and the desired unknown quantity.

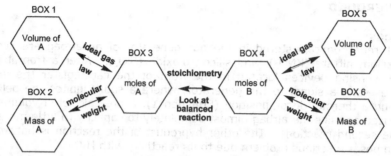

Figure 2. Flowchart for performing gas stoichiometry problems.

Sample problem: How many grams of NaN_3 must be decomposed to fill a 42.0 L airbag with nitrogen gas at a pressure of 1.05 atm and a temperature of 29.5°C?

Sample solution: Table 1 shows a method for solving gas stoichiometry problems. The method is broken down into 4 steps. The column on the left describes what is involved in each step and the column on the right shows the actual work for the sample problem. With a little practice these steps can be generalized and used to solve most dimensional analysis problems.

Table 1: Solution to Sample Problem

Step 1: Organize the problem	
Identify what is **known**.	**Known:** $2NaN_3(s) \rightarrow 2Na(s) + 3N_2(g)$ $V(N_2)=42.0$ L $\qquad$ $T(N_2)=29.5°C=302.5$ K $P(N_2)=1.05$ atm $\qquad$ $R=0.08206$ L•atm/K•mol
Identify **unknowns**.	**Unknown:** Moles of NaN_3? Mass of NaN_3?
Make a **prediction**.	**Prediction:** From the balanced chemical equation, the number of moles nitrogen gas produced is greater than the number of moles of sodium azide that decompose.
Step 2: Outline your problem using the flowchart in Figure 2	
Determine starting and ending points on the flow chart. Use these to plan an **outline** for your calculation.	**Outline:** We are given the volume of N_2 needed (corresponds to "volume of A" on the flow chart). This will be converted to moles of N_2 ("moles of A") using the ideal gas law. The moles of N_2 are then converted to moles of NaN_3 ("moles of B") using the stoichiometry from the balanced reaction. The number of grams of NaN_3 ("mass of B") is then determined.
Identify the appropriate **connections** to carry out your outline.	**Connections:** • To convert from volume of N_2 to moles of N_2, ("volume of A" to "moles of A") use: $n_{N2} = \dfrac{PV}{RT}$ • To convert from moles of N_2 to moles of NaN_3, ("moles of A" to "moles of B") use: $\dfrac{3 \text{ moles of } N_2}{2 \text{ moles of } NaN_3}$ • To convert from moles of NaN_3 to grams of NaN_3, ("moles

	of B" to "mass of B") use:	$\dfrac{65.02 \text{ g NaN}_3}{\text{mole NaN}_3}$

Step 3: Perform steps in outline making sure the units cancel.		
At this point you can either do all the steps as one, continuous dimensional analysis problem or perform each of the steps individually as shown in the example.	• Convert from volume of N_2 to moles of N_2 using the connection found in Step 2: $$\dfrac{(1.05 \text{ atm})(42.0 \text{ L})}{(0.08206 \text{ L atm/K mol})(302.5 \text{ K})} = 1.78 \text{ moles N}_2$$ • Convert from moles of N_2 to moles of NaN_3: $$1.78 \text{ moles N}_2 \bullet \dfrac{2 \text{ moles of NaN}_3}{3 \text{ moles of N}_2} = 1.18 \text{ moles NaN}_3$$ • Convert from moles of NaN_3 to grams of NaN_3: $$1.18 \text{ moles of NaN}_3 \bullet \dfrac{65.02 \text{ grams}}{1 \text{ mole of NaN}_3} = \mathbf{77.0 \text{ g NaN}_3}$$	

Step 4: Check your answer		
Correct units and significant figures?	Yes, the answer has three significant figures.	
Is the question answered?	Yes, the question asked to find the mass of NaN_3.	
Does the result make sense?	The answer agrees with the initial prediction. We expected the moles of moles N_2 to be greater than the moles of NaN_3.	

OVERVIEW

This experiment will be unlike previous procedures, because you will design your own protocol. Your assigned task is to simulate the automobile airbag by filling a plastic bag with gas. However, because sodium azide is extremely explosive and toxic, this experiment will not involve the actual reagents used in airbags. Instead the reaction that will be used to demonstrate gas stoichiometry is the reaction between sodium bicarbonate and acetic acid. This experiment will require detailed note taking, because you must formally write-up your procedure and results as part of your post-lab exercises.

PROCEDURE

Chemicals Used	Materials Used
Sodium bicarbonate 1 M Acetic acid	Small plastic zip lock bag Ruler 50-mL Graduated cylinder Analytical balance and weighing paper Scoopula Compressed air

Your first job as a researcher for an automobile company is trying to devise a new air bag that utilizes less expensive chemicals. You have decided to use the gas generated from the reaction of sodium bicarbonate with acetic acid to fill the plastic bag. As part of your work, you will need to calculate how much of each reagent is required to fill the bag with gas. Test your calculation by attempting to fill the baggie with gas. If the baggie does not fill to capacity (or is over filled), re-examine your calculations.

Your supervisor must know exactly what you did, how you did it, and how much of each reagent was used. Make sure that you take careful notes while performing this experiment.

Caution: When determining the volume of the plastic bag, remember that nothing in lab should be placed in or near your mouth. Since you can't blow up the bag using your lips or a straw, you must find another way to determine the volume of the bag.

Gas Stoichiometry: The Automobile Airbag

Name:	Lab Instructor:
Date:	Lab Section:

PRE-LABORATORY EXERCISES

1. The thermal decomposition of calcium carbonate produces two by-products, calcium oxide (also known as quicklime) and carbon dioxide. Calculate the volume of carbon dioxide produced at STP from the decomposition of 231 grams of calcium carbonate.

2. On December 1, 1783, Jacque Charles became the first human to pilot a non-tethered hydrogen balloon. He flew the balloon for fifteen miles and stayed in the air for a total flight time of 45 minutes. The balloon was made of silk coated with a thin layer of natural rubber and had a diameter of 27 feet. He generated the hydrogen gas needed to lift the balloon by mixing a large amount of iron with aqueous sulfuric acid. If he used 1×10^3 lbs. of iron and excess sulfuric acid, how many liters of hydrogen gas were made?

$$Fe\ (s) + H_2SO_4\ (aq) \rightarrow FeSO_4\ (aq) + H_2\ (g)$$

OVER →

PRE-LABORATORY EXERCISES continued...

3. Another process that is used to inflate things such as weather balloons, life rafts, etc. is the reaction between calcium hydride and water to give calcium hydroxide and hydrogen gas. How many grams of calcium hydride are needed to fill a life raft having a volume of 10.2 L and a pressure of 735 torr at 22°C?

4. Write the balanced chemical reaction that will be used to fill the air bag you make in this experiment. Hint: One of the products of the reaction between sodium bicarbonate (also called sodium hydrogen carbonate) and acetic acid is a gas.

Gas Stoichiometry: The Automobile Airbag

Name:	Lab Instructor:
Date:	Lab Section:

RESULTS and POST-LABORATORY QUESTIONS

For this experiment instead of having post-lab questions, you are required to write a laboratory report to prepare you for the type of work required in subsequent science courses. Unless instructed otherwise, follow the format given below for preparing your typed laboratory report.

I. Introduction
   a) Describe the goal of the experiment.
   b) Introduction to airbags (include a brief history of airbags, the purpose of airbags and how they function). For this section you will need to summarize an article on airbags. Record the reference for the article or the URL of the website where you found the information along with the date when you accessed the site.

II. Experimental
   a) Write the procedural protocol that you devised. Make sure to include a list of materials, the quantities of reagents and a detailed stepwise procedure. Include a description of how to determine the volume of the bag.

III. Results and Discussion
   a) Following the model in Table 1 in the background, show the gas stoichiometry calculation for your airbag.
   b) Describe the pros and cons of the particular chemical reaction used to inflate the airbag.
   c) Comment on the number of trials preformed, and how the experiment could be improved along with any experimental errors you made.

Limiting Reactants: How Much BaSO₄ Can We Make?

Holly Garrison

OBJECTIVES

- Be able to write and balance chemical equations.
- Perform calculations involving limiting reactants, theoretical yield, actual yield and percent yield.

INTRODUCTION

You have been asked to make ham and cheese sandwiches (Figure 1) for a group of children. Each sandwich requires two pieces of bread, one slice of ham, two slices of cheese, and one piece of lettuce. You have three loaves of bread each containing twenty-four slices, four packages of cheese containing sixteen slices each, six packages of ham each containing eight slices, and three heads of lettuce containing fourteen pieces. Which ingredient limits the number of sandwiches you can make? Which ingredients are in excess?

2 slices of bread + 1 slice of ham + 2 slices of cheese + 1 piece of lettuce = 1 sandwich

Figure 1. How many sandwiches you are able to make
depends on which ingredient you run out of first.

BACKGROUND

Referring to the sandwich example from the INTRODUCTION, we have certain amounts of the ingredients: three loaves of bread, four packages of cheese, six packages of ham, and three heads of lettuce. Given these specific quantities, we must determine which ingredient limits the number of sandwiches that can be produced. Because we know the specific ratio of ingredients per sandwich, the total number of sandwiches made from each ingredient can be calculated as a series of dimentional analysis steps:

$$3 \text{ loaves of bread} \times \frac{24 \text{ slices}}{1 \text{ loaf}} \times \frac{1 \text{ sandwich}}{2 \text{ slices of bread}} = 36 \text{ sandwiches}$$

$$4 \text{ packages of cheese} \times \frac{16 \text{ slices of cheese}}{1 \text{ package}} \times \frac{1 \text{ sandwich}}{2 \text{ slices of cheese}} = 32 \text{ sandwiches}$$

$$6 \text{ packages of ham} \times \frac{8 \text{ slices of ham}}{1 \text{ package}} \times \frac{1 \text{ sandwich}}{1 \text{ slice of ham}} = 48 \text{ sandwiches}$$

$$3 \text{ heads of lettuce} \times \frac{14 \text{ pieces of lettuce}}{1 \text{ head of lettuce}} \times \frac{1 \text{ sandwich}}{1 \text{ piece of lettuce}} = 42 \text{ sandwiches}$$

From our calculations we determine that the cheese is the ingredient (reactant) that yields the fewest sandwiches (lower amount of product). In chemical terminology, the cheese is the "limiting reactant". After the thirty-two possible sandwiches are made, the cheese is used up and there are excess quantities of bread, ham and lettuce.

Limiting Reactants

The example of producing sandwiches provides a non-chemical analogy for the chemical concept of limiting reactants. Until this point in your study of chemistry, you were typically given one reactant and asked to calculate the amount of product produced assuming that the other reactants were in excess. In those types of problems, you were actually being given the limiting reactant, without actually calling it by that name. Now you will learn what to do if you are given the masses of each reactant and you are required to determine which is the limiting reactant. In general, limiting reactant problems can be solved using the flowchart in Figure 2. The number of steps required for our work depends on our actual starting and ending places in the flow chart.

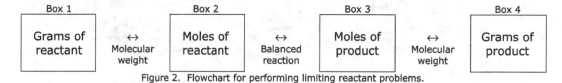

Figure 2. Flowchart for performing limiting reactant problems.

Sample problem: You are given 2.0 grams of zinc and 2.5 grams of silver nitrate and told that they react with each other as in Equation 1. What is the limiting reactant? How many grams of silver can be formed?

$$\text{Zn (s)} + 2 \text{ AgNO}_3 \text{ (aq)} \rightarrow 2 \text{ Ag (s)} + \text{Zn(NO}_3)_2 \text{ (aq)} \qquad \text{Equation 1}$$

Solution to Sample problem: As in the example of the sandwiches, in order to solve this problem, we must identify which species (Zn or $AgNO_3$) limits how much chlorine gas we can make. Table 1 shows a method for solving limiting reactant problems. The method is broken down into 4 steps. The column on the left describes what is involved in each step and the column on the right shows the actual work for the sample problem. With a little practice these steps can be generalized and used to solve most dimensional analysis problems.

Table 1: Solution to Sample Problem

Step 1: Organize the problem	
Identify what is **known**.	**Known:** $Zn(s) + 2AgNO_3(aq) \rightarrow 2Ag(s) + Zn(NO_3)_2(aq)$ Mass(Zn)=2.0 grams Mass($AgNO_3$)=2.5 grams
Identify **unknown**.	**Unknown:** Limiting reactant? Mass of Ag?
Make **prediction**.	**Prediction:** We have fewer grams of Zn, but the molar mass of Zn is so much less, that it probably corresponds to more moles than $AgNO_3$. That coupled with the fact that each mole of Zn generates two moles of Ag, suggests that the Zn is in excess and the $AgNO_3$ is the limiting reactant.
Step 2: Outline your problem using the flowchart in Figure 2	
Determine starting and ending points on the flow chart. Use these to plan an **outline** for your calculation.	**Outline:** We are given the mass of Zn provided (corresponds to "Box 1" on the flow chart). This will be converted to moles of Zn ("Box 2") using the molar mass. The moles of N_2 are then converted to moles of Ag ("Box 3") using the stoichiometry from the balanced reaction. The number of grams of Ag ("Box 4") is then determined. The entire process is then repeated using the mass of $AgNO_3$ in place of the Zn. The species that produces the smallest mass of Ag is the limiting reactant.
Identify the appropriate **connections** to carry out your outline.	**Connections:** **Assuming Zn is limiting reactant.** • To convert from mass of Zn to moles of Zn, ("Box 1" to "Box 2") use: $\dfrac{65.39 \text{ g Zn}}{\text{mole Zn}}$ • To convert from moles of Zn to moles of Ag, ("Box 2" to "Box 3") use: $\dfrac{1 \text{ mole of Zn}}{2 \text{ mole of Ag}}$ • To convert from moles of Ag to grams of Ag, ("Box 3" to "Box 4") use: $\dfrac{107.9 \text{ g Ag}}{\text{mole Ag}}$ **Assuming $AgNO_3$ is limiting reactant.** • To convert from mass of $AgNO_3$ to moles of $AgNO_3$, ("Box 1" to "Box 2") use: $\dfrac{169.9 \text{ g } AgNO_3}{\text{mole } AgNO_3}$ • To convert from moles of $AgNO_3$ to moles of Ag, ("Box 2" to "Box 3") use: $\dfrac{2 \text{ moles of } AgNO_3}{2 \text{ mole of Ag}}$ • To convert from moles of Ag to grams of Ag, ("Box 3" to "Box

4") use: $\dfrac{107.9 \text{ g Ag}}{\text{mole Ag}}$

Step 3: Perform steps in outline making sure the units cancel.	
At this point you can either do all the steps as one, continuous dimensional analysis problem or perform each of the steps individually as shown in the example.	**Assuming Zn is limiting reactant.** • Convert from mass of Zn to moles of Zn using the connection found in Step 2: $2.0 \text{ g Zn} \cdot \dfrac{1 \text{ mol Zn}}{65.39 \text{ g Zn}} = 0.0306 \text{ moles Zn}$ • Convert from moles of Zn to moles of Ag: $0.0306 \text{ moles Zn} \cdot \dfrac{2 \text{ mole of Ag}}{1 \text{ mole of Zn}} = 0.0612 \text{ moles Ag}$ • Convert from moles of Ag to grams of Ag: $0.0612 \text{ moles of Ag} \cdot \dfrac{107.9 \text{ g Ag}}{\text{mole Ag}} = \textbf{6.6 g Ag}$ **Assuming AgNO$_3$ is limiting reactant.** • Convert from mass of AgNO$_3$ to moles of AgNO$_3$ using the connection found in Step 2: $2.5 \text{ g AgNO}_3 \cdot \dfrac{1 \text{ mol AgNO}_3}{169.9 \text{ g AgNO}_3} = 0.0147 \text{ moles AgNO}_3$ • Convert from moles of AgNO$_3$ to moles of Ag: $0.0147 \text{ moles AgNO}_3 \cdot \dfrac{2 \text{ moles of Ag}}{2 \text{ mole of AgNO}_3} = 0.0147 \text{ moles Ag}$ • Convert from moles of Ag to grams of Ag: $0.0147 \text{ moles of AgNO}_3 \cdot \dfrac{107.9 \text{ g Ag}}{\text{mole Ag}} = \textbf{1.6 g Ag}$ **Because the AgNO$_3$ makes less Ag, the AgNO$_3$ is the limiting reactant. A total of 1.6 g of Ag are made.**

Step 4: Check your answer	
Correct **significant figures** and **units**?	Yes, the answer has two significant figures.
Is the **question answered**?	Yes, the question asked to find the limiting reactant and the mass of Ag.
Does the result **make sense**?	The answer agrees with the initial prediction. We expected the AgNO$_3$ to be the limiting reactant.

The amount of Ag calculated in the Sample problem is an example of a theoretical yield. The theoretical yield is the maximum product that can be expected if 100% of the limiting reactant is converted successfully to products. The theoretical yield is contrasted with the actual yield which is the real amount of the product that is made experimentally. If we carry out the reaction described in the Sample problem and we obtain an actual yield of 1.4 g of Ag, the percent yield is calculated using Equation 2.

$$\% \text{ yield} = \frac{\text{actual yield}}{\text{theoretical yield}} \times 100 = \frac{1.4 \text{ g Ag}}{1.6 \text{ g Ag}} \times 100 = 88 \%$$ Equation 2

OVERVIEW

In this experiment, you will combine sulfuric acid and aqueous barium chloride to produce a precipitate, barium sulfate and hydrochloric acid. The precipitate will be isolated by filtration and the theoretical yield will be calculated. You will predict the limiting reactant, and then verify your hypothesis in the lab.

PROCEDURE

Chemicals Used	Materials Used
0.20 M Barium chloride 0.60 M Sulfuric acid 1 M Hydrochloric acid Acetone	Heat resistant gloves Various pipets and pipet bulb 50-mL Ehrlenmeyer flasks (3) Glass stirring rod Hot plate Analytical balance Buchner funnel and filter paper Vacuum filtration apparatus (Figure 3) Ring stand and clamp Oven

1. Working in pairs, students will be assigned to work with one of the following volumes of 0.20 M barium chloride: 5, 10, 15, 20, 25 or 30 mLs. Two pairs of students will be assigned the same volume for comparison.

2. Pipet your assigned volume of 0.20 M barium chloride into a 50-mL flask. Warm the flask in the hood on a hot plate to near boiling.

3. Rinse your pipet with distilled water. Pipet 5.00 mL of 0.60 M sulfuric acid into another 50-mL flask. Again, rinse your pipet and add 5.00 mL of 1 M hydrochloric acid to the same flask. Warm this flask on a hot plate to near boiling.

4. While the solutions are heating, weigh a piece of filter paper and place it in the funnel. Moisten the filter paper with de-ionized water so that it adheres to the funnel. Place the funnel with the filter paper into the filtration apparatus with a rubber tube attached to a vacuum (Figure 3).

5. Work in the hood with heat resistant gloves. When both solutions are hot, slowly (while stirring) add the barium chloride to the flask with the sulfuric acid. Rinse any precipitate off the stirring rod into the flask with de-ionized water. Heat the solution for another 15 minutes to ensure formation of large crystals of precipitate. Add an additional 5 mLs of water as needed to prevent total evaporation. Allow the mixture to cool slowly to room temperature.

6. Pour the mixture onto the filter paper in the funnel. Rinse the residual precipitate into the funnel using de-ionized water. Turn on the vacuum for 3 minutes. Once the precipitate is fairly dry, add about 5 mLs of

Figure 3. Vacuum filtration apparatus.

acetone to the funnel to speed the drying. When the filter paper is dry, remove the paper and precipitate, and determine the mass of the paper and precipitate. Alternatively, the filter paper may be dried in a laboratory oven.

7. Before leaving, calculate the actual mass of barium sulfate that you isolated and add your results (averaged with the other group that use the same volume of barium chloride) to the blackboard for the class graph of "mass of barium sulfate made versus volume of barium chloride used".

Limiting Reactants: How Much BaSO₄ Can We Make?

Name:	Lab Instructor:
Date:	Lab Section:

PRE-LABORATORY EXERCISES

1. Write and balance the equation for the reaction you will be running as described in the OVERVIEW.

2. According to the concentrations in the PROCEDURE and assuming that you are assigned to work with 1 mL of barium chloride, calculate the theoretical number of grams of barium sulfate that should be produced. What is the limiting reactant? Write up your answer following the steps in Table 1 in the BACKGROUND.

OVER →

PRE-LABORATORY EXERCISES continued...

3. You allow 75.0 grams of carbon monoxide to react with 58.0 grams of hydrogen according to the following process. Determine the limiting reactant and the amount of methanol produced. Again, show your work following the steps in Table 1.

$$CO\ (g) + H_2\ (g) \rightarrow CH_3OH\ (l)$$

Limiting Reactants: How Much BaSO₄ Can We Make?

Name:	Lab Instructor:
Date:	Lab Section:

RESULTS and POST-LABORATORY QUESTIONS

Assigned volume of barium chloride

Actual mass of barium sulfate isolated

1. Calculate the theoretical yield of barium sulfate using your assigned volume.

2. Calculate the percent yield of barium sulfate.

3. Attach a copy of the graph of the average class data for "mass of barium sulfate made versus volume of barium chloride used". What is occurring before the graph levels off? What is indicated after the graph levels off?

Colligative Properties: Analysis of Freezing Point Depression

Kristen Spotz

OBJECTIVES

- Verify experimentally that colligative properties depend on the number of solute particles and not on the solute's identity.
- Perform a detailed analysis of the freezing point depression of cyclohexane.

INTRODUCTION

You wake up one chilly January morning. The temperature is −5.0°C outside and you wonder whether your car will start. You walk outside and find your car surrounded by snow. To your surprise your car does start thanks to the antifreeze, ethylene glycol ($C_2H_6O_2$), you added to your car's radiator (Figure 1).

Similarly, arctic fish require a form of biological antifreeze, typically glycerol ($C_3H_8O_3$), to help prevent their blood from freezing (Figure 2).

Who would have thought that an automobile radiator and an arctic fish would have so much in common?

Figure 1. Adding antifreeze to a car's radiator is a necessity in cold climates

Figure 2. A cold-loving arctic fish.

Background

When a non-volatile solute is added to a solvent, the resulting solution has different physical properties than the pure solvent. Going back to our antifreeze example, the pure solvent, water, has a freezing point of 0°C. When we add a non-volatile solute such as ethylene glycol, CH_2OHCH_2OH, the freezing point of the solution is lowered. Surprisingly, the amount the freezing point lowers depends only on the quantity of solute particles added and not on the actual identity of the solute added. There are four such properties, known as colligative properties, that are dependent on the amount of solute: vapor pressure lowering, boiling point elevation, freezing point depression, and osmotic pressure. The basis for the colligative properties lies in the inability of the solvent particles to join the solvent in moving between phases or through a semipermeable membrane, in the case of osmotic pressure.

Since the focus is on the number of solute particles added, we must account for the fact that in cases where the solutes are electrolytes, the formula of the solute must be taken into account. For example adding 1.0 mole of NaCl to a liter of water has the effect of actually adding 2.0 moles of particles (1.0 mole of Na^+ ions and 1.0 mole of Cl^- ions).

Vapor Pressure Lowering

The vapor pressure of a solution containing a non-volatile solute is always less than the vapor pressure of the pure solvent. This concept can be explained in terms of entropy, which is the measure of the system's disorder. Processes in nature tend to occur in the direction of increasing disorder. The molecules in the liquid phase are closer together and more ordered than the molecules in the gas phase. Therefore, the entropy of a pure liquid increases as the molecules vaporize. This process continues until the system reaches a dynamic equilibrium at which point the molecules are vaporizing and condensing at the same rate. At this point the vapor pressure is accessed (Figure 3a). However, when a nonvolatile solute is dissolved in a solvent, the resulting solution is more disordered than the pure liquid with which you began. The solvent in the solution has less of a tendency to vaporize and equilibrium is established at a lower vapor pressure (Figure 3b).

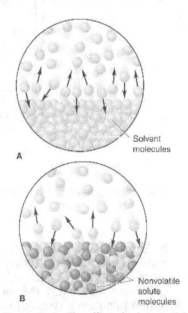

Solvent molecules

A

Nonvolatile solute molecules

B

Figures 3a,b. The effect of solute particles on the vapor pressure of a liquid.

We can also consider the decrease in the vapor pressure of a solution in more simplistic terms. The dissolved nonvolatile solute decreases the number of solvent molecules on the solution's surface that are capable of vaporizing. In a sense, the solute acts to "block" the solvent molecules in the liquid phase from entering the vapor phase, resulting in a decreased vapor pressure.

Boiling Point Elevation

Under normal conditions, pure water boils at 100.00 °C. However, if 18.0 grams of glucose is dissolved in 150 mL of water, the resulting solution boils at 100.34 °C. This increase in boiling point can be explained by examining the phase diagram for water (Figure 4). The boiling point of a liquid is the temperature where the vapor pressure of the liquid equals the atmospheric pressure. At this point, the liquid and vapor phase molecules are in equilibrium. Start by locating the temperature corresponding to the boiling point of water in

Figure 4. Notice that at this temperature, the vapor pressure of the water is 1 atm. As long as the atmospheric pressure is also 1 atm, the water will boil. You should notice that at the same temperature, the vapor pressure of the solution (dotted line) is less than 1 atm. Therefore, to boil the solution, temperature must be increased (by ΔT_b) in order to raise the vapor pressure of the solution until it is also equal to the atmospheric pressure.

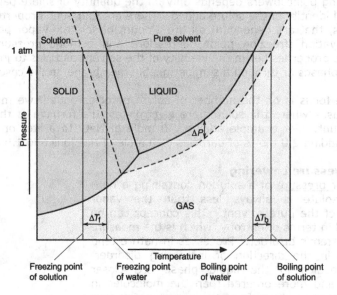

Figure 4. The phase diagram of pure water overlaid with the phase diagram of an aqueous solution.

The magnitude of the boiling point elevation can be calculated using Equation 1:

$$\Delta T_b = K_b m \qquad\qquad \text{Equation 1}$$

In Equation 1, ΔT_b is the difference between the boiling point of the pure solvent and the boiling point of the solution (°C), K_b is the molal boiling-point-elevation constant (°C/m), which is specific for each solvent, and m is the <u>molality</u> of the solution. Scientists can utilize Equation 1 to identify the molar mass of an unknown solute or to predict how much solute to add to obtain a required temperature change.

Freezing Point Depression

Freezing point depression is quantified by an equation similar in form to Equation 1. The actual freezing point is difficult to determine, however, by direct visual observation because of a phenomenon known as supercooling. With supercooling, a liquid being slowly cooled can remain liquid below its freezing point because the molecules are unable to orient themselves into the crystalline array characteristic of a solid. Constant stirring is utilized to reduce the effect of supercooling and to prevent an incorrect freezing point reading. In addition, a temperature-time graph or cooling curve (Figure 5) will be used to more accurately determine the freezing points of the solvent and solution.

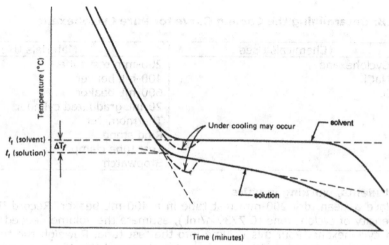

Figure 5. Cooling curve for solvent and solution.

The above cooling curve is generated by plotting temperature as a function of time for both the pure solvent and the solution. The freezing point of both the pure solvent and the solution is determined through extrapolation.

OVERVIEW

The nature of colligative properties will be explored by observing what happens to the freezing point of water after adding several different solutes. Your in depth study of the freezing point depression of cyclohexane will begin by constructing a cooling curve for pure cyclohexane.   Half the class will then construct a cooling curve for a solution of naphthalene in cyclohexane while the other half of the class constructs a cooling curve for a solution of an unknown solute in cyclohexane. Information drawn from these curves will allow for the calculation of the molal freezing-point-depression constant for cyclohexane as well as the molar mass of the unknown solute.

PROCEDURE

Part A: Confirming the Nature of Colligative Properties

Chemicals Used	Materials Used
Urea (1.8 g)	Styrofoam cups (3)
Glucose (5.4 g)	Analytical balance
Sodium chloride (0.90 g)	Spatula
Ice	Thermometer

All students, working in pairs
Half-fill a Styrofoam cup with ice. Record the initial temperature of the ice. Add 1.8 g of urea to the cup. Stir until the urea is dissolved. Record the final, lowest temperature of the mixture. Repeat with 5.4 g of glucose and again with 0.9 g of sodium chloride. Dispose of the urea solution according to your instructor's directions.

Part B: Determining the Cooling Curve for Pure Cyclohexane

Chemicals Used	Materials Used
Cyclohexane NaCl Ice	200-mm test tube 400-mL beaker 600-mL beaker 20-mL graduated cylinder Thermometer Ring stand Test tube clamp Stopwatch

All students, working in pairs

1. Place a clean, dry 200-mm test tube in a 400-mL beaker. Record the mass. Using the density of cyclohexane (0.7739 g/mL), estimate the volume needed for about 10 grams of cyclohexane. Pour this volume into the test tube. Reweigh the test tube, the beaker and the cyclohexane. Wrap a paper towel around the 400-mL beaker and place inside the 600-mL beaker. Fill the 400-mL beaker completely full with ice. Add approximately 2 grams of NaCl to the ice.

2. Place the 600-mL beaker containing the ice bath and the test tube on a ring stand. Attach a test tube clamp to the ring stand to hold the test tube. Lower the thermometer completely into the test tube filled with cyclohexane.

3. While **constantly stirring** the cyclohexane with a thermometer, record the temperature (±0.2°C) at 20 second intervals. Once the cyclohexane solidifies, the temperature remains virtually constant. Continue collecting data at 20 second intervals until the temperature begins to drop again (typically after a total of 10 minutes).

4. Allow the cyclohexane to melt before reusing in Part C or D.

Part C: Determining the K_f for Cyclohexane

Chemicals Used	Materials Used
Naphthalene ($C_{10}H_8$) NaCl Ice	Cooling curve apparatus (from Part B) Spatula Analytical balance Stopwatch

Half the class, working in pairs

Measure approximately 0.30 grams of naphthalene (record the actual mass used) and transfer into the test tube filled with cyclohexane that you used in Part B. Make sure the naphthalene is completely dissolved before proceeding to the next section. Add ice and salt to the 400-mL beaker as needed.

Determine the freezing point of the solution in the same way you did for the pure solvent. Again, be sure to collect data for at least 10 minutes. Dispose of the cyclohexane solution according to your instructor's directions.

Part D: Determining the Molar Mass of an Unknown Solute

Chemicals Used	Materials Used
Unknown solute	Cooling curve apparatus (from Part B)
NaCl	Spatula
Ice	Analytical balance
	Stopwatch

Half the class, working in pairs
Measure approximately 0.30 grams of unknown (record the actual mass used) and transfer into the test tube filled with cyclohexane that you used in Part B. Make sure the unknown is completely dissolved before proceeding to the next section. Add ice and salt to the 400-mL beaker as needed.

Determine the freezing point of the solution in the same way you did for the pure solvent. Again, be sure to collect data for at least 10 minutes. Dispose of the cyclohexane solution according to your instructor's directions.

Part E: Group work

All students, working in pairs
Students who did Part C: graph your data. Determine the freezing point. From the data in Part B and Part C, determine the freezing point depression. Write your value of K_f on the board with the class data. Before you leave, copy all of the class data.

Students who did Part D: graph your data. Determine the freezing point. From the data in Part B and Part D, determine the freezing point depression. Using the class average for K_f (from Part C), calculate the molar mass of the unknown. Before you leave, write your value for the molar mass on the board and copy all of the class data.

Colligative Properties: Analysis of Freezing Point Depression

Name:	Lab Instructor:
Date:	Lab Section:

PRE-LABORATORY EXCERCISES

1. Define the <u>underlined</u> terms in the BACKGROUND section.

2. Is the following statement TRUE or FALSE: "Dissolving a nonvolatile solute in a solvent has the effect of extending the temperature range over which the solvent remains in the liquid phase." Explain.

3. Write the equation for the freezing point depression (similar to Equation 1).

4. Describe a practical application of the freezing point depression (other than the ones already given in the INTRODUCTION and BACKGROUND).

OVER →

PRE-LABORATORY EXCERCISES continued...

5. Assuming that each system behaves ideally, which solution (0.25 m KCl or 0.25 m $C_3H_8O_3$) would have the lower freezing point? Explain.

6. What is the boiling point of the water in your radiator if 2.00 kg of antifreeze (ethylene glycol, $C_2H_6O_2$) is added to 9.00×10^3 grams of water?

Colligative Properties: Analysis of Freezing Point Depression

Name:	Lab Instructor:
Date:	Lab Section:

RESULTS and POST-LABORATORY QUESTIONS

Part A: Confirming the Nature of Colligative Properties

Solute	Formula	Grams used	Moles of particles	Initial Temp.	Final Temp.
Urea					
Glucose					
Sodium Chloride					

What conclusions can you draw by comparing the freezing points of the solutions of urea and glucose? Explain.

What conclusions can you draw by comparing the freezing points of the solutions of urea and sodium chloride? Explain.

Part B: Determining the Cooling Curve for Pure Cyclohexane
Mass of cyclohexane used
Freezing point of cyclohexane (from curve)
Attach a copy of your cooling curve

Part C and D
Which part did you and your laboratory partner perform? (Circle one)   Part C   or   Part D

	Part C	Part D
Freezing point of solution (from curve)		
Freezing pt. depression, ΔT_f		
Mass of solute added		
Moles of solute added		
Mass of solvent, kg		
Molality of solution		
Your value of K_f for cyclohexane		
Class average for K_f for cyclohexane		
Your value of molar mass of unknown		
Class average of molar mass of unknown		

Attach a copy of your cooling curve

OVER →

22–9

RESULTS and POST-LABORATORY QUESTIONS continued...

1. Which of the following substances would be most efficient per unit mass at melting snow from sidewalks and roads: glucose, sodium chloride, ethylene glycol, or calcium nitrate. Your explanation should include possible environmental impact.

2. Pure benzene has a normal freezing point of 5.50°C. A solution containing 11.4 grams of a molecular substance dissolved in 150.0 grams of benzene (K_f = 5.12°C/m) has a freezing point of 1.20°C. What is the molar mass of the solute?

3. If you had incorrectly read the freezing point of the solution in POST-LABORATORY QUESTION #2 to be 0.30°C lower than the true freezing point of the solution, would the calculated molar mass of the solute by too high or too low? Explain.

Experiment 15

15

Antacid Analysis

And the Determination of the Percent Acetic Acid in Vinegar

PURPOSE AND LEARNING OBJECTIVES

To use acid-base titration as a method to determine the percent acetic acid in vinegar and to determine the neutralization capacity of antacid tablets. To learn the technique of standardizing a solution.

PRINCIPLES

According to Bronsted-Lowry definition of acids and bases, an acid is a proton (H^+) donor and a base is a proton acceptor. However, there is more than one way to define acids and bases. According to Arrhenius, a base is defined as a substance that, when dissolved in water, increases the concentration of the hydroxide ion, OH^-, over that in pure water. An acid is defined as a substance that, when dissolved in water, increases the concentration of the hydrogen ion, H^+, over that in pure water. The reaction of an acid with a base produces a salt and water, a process known as neutralization. For example, the reaction of hydrochloric acid with sodium hydroxide produces sodium chloride and water.

$$HCl\ (aq) + NaOH\ (aq) \rightarrow NaCl\ (aq) + H_2O\ (l)$$

This reaction can also be written as the total ionic equation to show which species are present in solution and the net ionic equation which clearly shows the neutralization reaction.

Total Ionic Equation: H^+ (aq) + ~~Cl^-~~ (aq) + ~~Na^+~~ (aq) + OH^- (aq) → ~~Na^+~~ (aq) + ~~Cl^-~~ (aq) + H_2O (l)

Net Ionic Equation: H^+ (aq) + OH^- (aq) → H_2O (l)

pH Scale

In aqueous solutions, the concentration of the hydrogen ion, $[H^+]$, can range from very large values, 10.0 M, to very small values, 1.0×10^{-15} M. To compress this large range in values, a logarithmic scale is used. This is called the pH scale. The pH of a solution is defined as the negative logarithm of the hydrogen ion concentration.

$$pH = -\log [H^+] \quad \text{or} \quad [H^+] = 10^{-pH}$$

Water autoionizes to a small but measurable extent to produce H^+ and OH^- according to the following equation.

$$H_2O \text{ (l)} \rightleftharpoons H^+ \text{ (aq)} + OH^- \text{ (aq)} \qquad K_w = [H^+][OH^-] = 1 \times 10^{-14} \text{ at } 25°C$$

$$[H^+] = [OH^-] = 1.0 \times 10^{-7} M$$

When $[H^+] = [OH^-]$, the solution is said to be neutral (neither acidic or basic). That is, pH = – log$[H^+]$ = – log(1.0 x 10^{-7}) = 7.00. Thus, the pH of a neutral solution is 7.00. When the pH of a solution is less than 7 it is acidic, and if it is greater than 7 it is basic.

pH	<	7	$[H^+]$ > $[OH^-]$	acidic solution
pH	=	7	$[H^+]$ = $[OH^-]$	neutral solution
pH	>	7	$[H^+]$ < $[OH^-]$	basic solution

Strong Acid-Strong Base Titration

A titration is used to determine the concentration of either an acid or a base. If the concentration of either an acid or base is known, the concentration of the other can then be determined. The solution of known concentration is placed in a burette and added to a solution of unknown concentration until the equivalence point is reached. In this experiment a strong acid, HCl, is titrated with a strong base, NaOH. HCl is a monoprotic acid, it donates a single proton. The stoichiometric ratio of HCl reacting with NaOH is one to one.

$$H^+ \text{ (aq)} + OH^- \text{ (aq)} \rightarrow H_2O \text{ (l)}$$

Thus, at the equivalence point the number of moles of hydroxide ions is equal to the number of moles of hydrogen ions.

At the equivalence point: moles of H^+ = moles of OH^-

The equivalence point is shown by a change in some physical property, such as a change in color. In colorless reactions an indicator is used to signal the equivalence point. An indicator is a substance that changes color dramatically with one drop of additional titrant. Phenolphthalein is an indicator which is colorless in acidic solution and violet in basic solution at pH > 8.2. Thymol blue is an indicator that has two end points. It is pink in acidic solution with pH < 2, turns yellow in acidic solution when pH ≈ 3.0, and is blue in basic solution, pH > 9.0.

Weak Acid-Strong Base Titration

Unlike strong acids, weak acids dissociate less than 1% in aqueous solution. In titrating a weak acid, HA, with a strong base such as NaOH, the acid HA reacts with OH^- according to the following reaction.

$$HA \ (aq) \ + \ OH^- \ (aq) \ \rightarrow \ A^- \ (aq) \ + \ H_2O \ (l)$$

At the equivalence point in the titration the moles of acid equals the moles of hydroxide ions.

At the equivalence point: moles of HA = moles of OH^-

Thus, by titrating a sample of vinegar with NaOH of known concentration, the concentration of acetic acid in the vinegar can be determined.

Titration of Antacids

In this experiment the neutralization capacity of stomach antacids, such as Tums and Rolaids, will be determined. The active ingredients in antacids include $Mg(OH)_2$, $CaCO_3$, or a combination of both. These are bases and dissociate to increase OH^- in solution.

$$Mg(OH)_2 \ (s) \ \rightleftharpoons \ Mg_2^+ \ (aq) \ + \ 2 \ OH^- \ (aq) \qquad K_{sp} = [Mg^{2+}][OH^-]^2$$

In contrast to the $Mg(OH)_2$, which produces OH^- directly upon dissociation, the $CaCO_3$ dissociates in water to produce the carbonate ion, CO_3^{2-}, which reacts with water to produce OH^-.

$$CaCO_3 \ (s) \ \rightleftharpoons \ Ca^{2+} \ (aq) \ + \ CO_3^{2-} \ (aq) \qquad K_{sp} = [Ca^{2+}][CO_3^{2-}]$$

$$CO_3^{2-} \ (aq) \ + \ H_2O \ (l) \ \rightleftharpoons \ HCO_3^- \ (aq) \ + \ OH^- \ (aq) \qquad K_b = \frac{[HCO_3^-][OH^-]}{[CO_3^{2-}]}$$

$$HCO_3^- \ (aq) \ + \ H_2O \ (l) \ \rightleftharpoons \ H_2CO_3 \ (aq) \ + \ OH^- \ (aq) \qquad K_b = \frac{[H_2CO_3][OH^-]}{[HCO_3^-]}$$

Thus, an aqueous solution of the antacid could be titrated directly with an acid. However, both $Mg(OH)_2$ and $CaCO_3$ are relatively insoluble in water, the solubility product constants, K_{sp}, are small, 1.2×10^{-11} and 8.7×10^{-9}, respectively. To get around this problem, a procedure called back-titration is used. In back-titration, the antacid is dissolved in excess acid, in this experiment HCl is used. Stomach acid is 0.14 M HCl. The base in the antacid reacts with the HCl. Because an excess of HCl is added, some HCl remains in solution. The solution is titrated with a base to determine the concentration of excess HCl. By subtracting the excess HCl from the original volume of HCl added, the amount of HCl consumed by the antacid is determined. This back-titration method is an accurate way to determine the neutralization capacity of the antacid.

The titration curve for the back-titration of an antacid containing $CaCO_3$ is shown in the figure 1. A standardized 3 M NaOH solution is used as the titrant and thymol blue as the indicator. The thymol blue indicator was chosen because the first end point occurs at pH $\approx$ 3, where the color changes from red to yellow. Due to the sharp increase in pH, the second end point, signaled by a change in color from yellow to blue, occurs immediately after the first end point. The first end point is not as sharp, changing slowly from red at pH $\approx$ 1.0 to peach at pH $\approx$ 1.5 to yellow at pH $\approx$ 3.0. However, even if the first end point is missed, the second end point is within 0.2 to 0.5 mL of the first end point, as shown in figure 1.

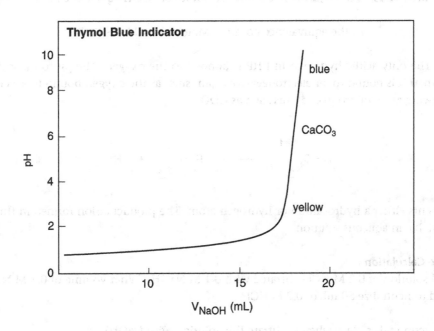

Figure 1. After 50 mL of 0.3 M HCl was added to dissolve the antacid tablet containing $CaCO_3$, the excess acid is titrated with standardized 0.3 M NaOH. The thymol blue indicator is red/pink in acidic solution. The solution is titrated to the yellow endpoint. One to two additional drops of 0.3 M NaOH turns the solution blue.

Standardization of NaOH Solution

In this experiment the solution of NaOH will be standardized to determine its exact concentration. In the standardization process, a sample of potassium hydrogen phthalate (abbreviated as KHP) is accurately weighed and dissolved in water. KHP is a monoprotic acid, donating a single proton in its reaction with the NaOH.

KHP ($C_8H_5O_4K$)

The KHP solution is titrated with the NaOH. In this reaction, 1 mole of NaOH reacts with 1 mole of KHP. Thus, at the equivalence point, the moles of NaOH equals the moles of KHP.

At the equivalence point: Moles OH^- = Moles KHP

NOTE: The only acidic hydrogen in KHP is bonded to the oxygen. The proton is lost more easily when it is bound to an electronegative atom, such as the oxygen bound to an electron withdrawing atom or group of atoms such as COO^-.

R represents either a hydrocarbon or hydrogen atom. The product anion formed in this reaction is stable in aqueous solution.

Example Calculation

A 50 ml solution of 0.2 M HCl is titrated with 0.1 M NaOH. What volume of 0.1 M NaOH is required to neutralize 50 mL of 0.2 M HCl?

What reaction takes place when we titrate this solution with NaOH?

Molecular Equation: HCl (aq) + NaOH (aq)   →   NaCl (aq) + H_2O (l)

Net Ionic Equation: H^+ (aq) + OH^- (aq)   → H_2O (l)

If we calculate the moles of H^+ initially in 50 mL of 0.2 M HCl, we can determine the moles of OH^- needed to neutralize the moles of H^+.

The concentration of HCl is 0.2 M. Square brackets are generally used to indicate concentration:

$$[HCl] = 0.2 \text{ M} = 0.2 \frac{\text{moles}}{\text{L}}$$

To determine the moles of HCl in solution, simply multiply the concentration by the volume.

$$\text{moles of HCl} = [HCl] \, V_{HCl} = \left(0.2 \frac{\text{moles}}{\text{L}} \right) 0.050 \text{ L} = 0.01 \text{ moles HCl}$$

HCl dissociates in water according to the following equation:

$$HCl \text{ (aq)} \quad \rightarrow \quad H^+ \text{ (aq)} + Cl^- \text{ (aq)}$$

Thus, 1 mole of HCl produces 1 mole of H^+.

$$0.01 \text{ moles HCl} \left(\frac{1 \text{ mol } H^+}{1 \text{ mol HCl}} \right) = 0.01 \text{ mol } H^+$$

The number of moles of OH^- needed to neutralize 0.01 mol of H^+ is calculated using the neutralization reaction.

$$H^+ \text{ (aq)} + OH^- \text{ (aq)} \quad \rightarrow \quad H_2O \text{ (l)}$$

Because 1 mole of H^+ reacts with 1 mole of OH^-, it takes 0.01 moles of OH^- to neutralize 0.01 moles of H^+.

$$0.01 \text{ moles } H^+ \left(\frac{1 \text{ mol } OH^-}{1 \text{ mol } H^+} \right) = 0.01 \text{ mol } OH^-$$

Finally we need to determine the volume of NaOH used. According to the following reaction, 1 mole of NaOH produces 1 mol of OH^-.

$$NaOH \text{ (aq)} \quad \rightarrow \quad Na^+ \text{ (aq)} + OH^- \text{ (aq)}$$

$$V_{NaOH} = \frac{0.01 \text{ mol NaOH}}{0.1 \text{ mol} / \text{L}} = 0.1 \text{ L} \qquad 0.1 \text{ L} \left(\frac{1000 \text{ mL}}{\text{L}} \right) = 100 \text{ mL}$$

Thus, if 0.01 mol of OH⁻ is needed to neutralize 0.01 mol of H⁺, 0.01 moles of NaOH was used. The volume of NaOH is calculated by dividing the moles of NaOH by its concentration.

It takes 100 ml of 0.1 M NaOH to neutralize 50 ml of 0.2 M HCl.

SAFETY
WEAR SAFETY GLASSES!!!

Take caution when working with potassium hydrogen phthalate (KHP). It is an irritant! NaOH is a strong base and HCl is a strong acid and can burn your skin and clothing if contact is made. In case of contact, flush with water immediately.

PROCEDURE
This experiment will be performed in pairs. It is important to stay consistent when taking measurements. One partner reads the burette until the titration is complete; the other partner reads the burette for the next titration.

Part 1. Standardization of NaOH Solution
1. Weigh and record three samples of potassium hydrogen phthalate (KHP) between 1.2 and 1.8 g to the nearest 0.001 g. Put the samples in three separate, labeled Erlenmeyer flasks, indicate the mass of KHP on each flask. Add 50.0 mL of DI water to each flask.

2. Warm the KHP solutions with a low flame Bunsen burner until the KHP is completely dissolved. **Do not boil the KHP solutions.** Let solutions cool to room temperature.

3. In a 500-mL Erlenmeyer flask, prepare 500.0 mL of 0.3 M NaOH solution starting from 6 M NaOH. The amount of 6 M NaOH needed was calculated in your pre-lab. The volume of the NaOH solution does not have to be known accurately because this solution will be titrated to determine the exact concentration. Stopper the flask.

    NOTE: The NaOH solution must be stoppered when not in use because the NaOH slowly reacts with CO_2 (g) in the air to produce carbonic acid, H_2CO_3.

    $$CO_2 \text{ (g)} + H_2O \text{ (l)} \rightarrow H_2CO_3 \text{ (aq)}$$

The carbonic acid dissociates to increase the H⁺ concentration in solution.

    $$H_2CO_3 \text{ (aq)} \rightleftharpoons HCO_3^- \text{ (aq)} + H^+ \text{ (aq)}$$

    $$HCO_3^- \text{ (aq)} \rightleftharpoons CO_3^{2-} \text{ (aq)} + H^+ \text{ (aq)}$$

H$^+$ (aq) reacts with OH$^-$ (aq) in solution, decreasing the concentration of OH$^-$, which would affect the end point in the titration.

$$H^+ \text{ (aq)} + OH^- \text{ (aq)} \quad \rightarrow \quad H_2O \text{ (l)}$$

4. Clean a 50.0 mL burette with soap and water. Do a final rinse of the burette with DI water. Make sure to run water through the tip of the burette. If the burette is clean water runs uniformly down the burette without adhering to the glass.

5. Rinse the burette with two 5 mL portions of the 0.3 M NaOH solution. Drain some of the NaOH through the tip.

6. Fill the burette with the NaOH solution to the zero mark or below the zero mark. If the burette is filled above the zero mark drain some of the solution into an empty 600-mL beaker (this beaker will be your waste beaker for the lab). To make sure there are no air bubbles in the tip, briefly open the stopcock to drain some of the solution through the tip and into your waste beaker.

7. Allow the solution to sit for a minute so all of the liquid settles in the burette. Read and record the initial volume of the NaOH in the burette.

8. Select one of the flasks containing KHP. Record the mass of KHP in your notebook.

9. Add two drops of 0.1% phenolphthalein to each of the KHP solutions and swirl.

10. Slowly titrate the KHP solution with sodium hydroxide solution while gently swirling the flask. As the NaOH solution is added a pink color will appear in the KHP solution. When the KHP solution is swirled the color disappears. As the end point is approached the pink disappears more slowly at which point the base should be added drop wise until the solution remains pink when swirled. A single drop can be sufficient to reach the end point. Remove any hanging drops from the burette tip by rinsing the tip with DI water into the flask, using a squirt bottle.

11. Once the end point is reached, record the final volume of the NaOH solution in the burette.

12. Repeat steps 6-11 for the other two KHP samples. At least two of the NaOH concentrations determined have to be the same, within 1.0 %.

13. Calculate the molarity of each of the NaOH solutions.

	Trial 1	Trial 2	Trial 3
Mass of KHP			
Moles of KHP			
Initial Burette Volume NaOH (mL)			
Final Burette Volume NaOH (mL)			
Total Volume of NaOH (mL)			
Moles of NaOH			
Molarity of NaOH (mol/L)			

14. Calculate the average molarity of NaOH and the average deviation.

Average Molarity:	
Average Deviation:	

Part 2. Titration of Vinegar

1. Fill the burette with the standardized 0.3 M NaOH. Read and record the initial volume.

2. Using a graduated cylinder, measure 20 mL of vinegar and place it in a 250 mL Erlenmeyer flask. Add two drops of 0.1% phenolphthalein.

3. Titrate the vinegar with the 0.3 M NaOH until the end point (faint pink color) is reached.

4. Repeat the above procedure until you get two determinations of the percent acetic acid in vinegar that are the same within 5 to 10 %.

	Trial 1	Trial 2	Trial 3
Volume of Vinegar (mL)			
Initial Burette Volume NaOH (mL)			
Final Burette Volume NaOH (mL)			
Total Volume of NaOH (mL)			
Moles of NaOH			
Moles of CH$_3$COOH in Vinegar (mol/L)			
Molarity of NaOH (mol/L)			
% acetic acid in Vinegar = $\left(\dfrac{[\text{CH}_3\text{COOH}]\ \text{in vinegar}}{17.4\ \text{M Glacial CH}_3\text{COOH}} \right) 100$			

Part 3. Titration of Antacid Tablets

1. Weigh and record the mass of one tablet of antacid to the nearest 0.001g. Record the brand of antacid used. Transfer the tablet to an Erlenmeyer flask; add 50 mL of 0.3 M HCl. Gently heat the solution on a hot plate, or over a low Bunsen burner flame, until the tablet is dissolved. Some solid residue may remain. This is most likely due to starch binders added to the antacid tablets.

2. Cool the antacid solution to room temperature by putting the bottom of the Erlenmeyer flask under running tap water. Add 10 drops of 0.1% thymol blue indicator. Thymol blue is red when the solution is very acidic (pH < 2). If your solution is not red add 10.0 mL more of the 0.3 M HCl in order to consume all the base in the antacid and to have excess acid present in solution. **Record the total volume of HCl added.**

3. Titrate the acidic antacid solution with 0.3 M NaOH to the yellow end point (pH = 3). Watch the color change carefully. The solution will turn pink, then a faded pink and peach. At this point add the basic solution drop-wise until the yellow end point is reached. After the first end point, one or two drops will turn the solution blue, which is the second end point. Record both end points.

4. Repeat the titration for another brand of antacid.

Data	Antacid 1	Antacid 2
Brand of antacid tablet		
Mass of antacid tablet (g)		
Total volume 0.3 M HCl added (mL)		
Millimoles of HCl		
Initial volume in burette (mL)		
Final Volume in the burette (mL)		
Total Volume of NaOH titrated (mL)		
Millimoles of NaOH		
Millimoles HCl reacted with base in antacid		
Identify the active ingredient in the antacid from the manufacturer's label.		
Write the balanced equation for the base in the antacid reacting with HCl.		
Millimoles of $CaCO_3$ in antacid		
Calculate the mass of the active ingredient in the antacid tablet.		
Calculate the % composition of active ingredient in the antacid		

■ **EXPERIMENT 15**

PRE-LAB QUESTIONS

1. Write the neutralization reaction for a strong acid-strong base titration, where HCl (aq) reacts with NaOH (aq).

2. Write the net ionic equation for the neutralization reaction in question 1.

3. Define the equivalence point in a strong acid-strong base titration.

4. In Part 1 of this experiment, what is the purpose of standardizing the solution of 0.3 M NaOH? If you take a reagent bottle of 0.3 M NaOH from the storeroom, does this mean it is 0.300 M? Is there a possibility that it is 0.27 M?

5. Explain why only one hydrogen is acidic in KHP.

KHP ($C_8H_5O_4K$)

6. KHP is titrated with NaOH until the equivalence point is reached. Why is it true that, the number of moles of OH^- equals the number of moles of KHP, at the equivalence point?

7. You will standardize a 0.3 M NaOH solution. Why must the solution be stoppered?

8. In Part 2 of this experiment, you will determine the percent acetic acid in vinegar. Acetic acid, CH_3COOH, is a weak acid. Write the net ionic equation for the following reaction:

$$CH_3COOH\ (aq) + NaOH\ (aq)\ \rightarrow\ NaCH_3COO\ (aq) + H_2O\ (l)$$

9. Write the neutralization reaction for a weak acid-strong base titration. Use HA to represent the weak acid and NaOH to represent the strong base.

10. Define the equivalence point in a weak acid-strong base titration.

11. In Part 3, you will analyze antacids for the active ingredients, $Mg(OH)_2$ and $CaCO_3$.

    a)   Write the equilibrium constant expression for the following reaction:

$$Mg(OH)_2 \text{ (s)} \quad \rightleftharpoons \quad Mg^{2+} \text{ (aq)} + 2\ OH^- \text{(aq)}$$

    b)   If any species are not included in the equilibrium constant expression, explain why they are not included.

12. Write the equilibrium constant expression for each of the following reactions:

$$CaCO_3 \text{ (s)} \quad \rightleftharpoons \quad Ca^{2+} \text{ (aq)} + CO_3^{2-} \text{ (aq)}$$

$$CO_3^{2-} \text{ (aq)} + H_2O \text{ (l)} \quad \rightleftharpoons \quad HCO_3^- \text{ (aq)} + OH^- \text{ (aq)}$$

$$HCO_3^- \text{ (aq)} + H_2O \text{ (l)} \quad \rightleftharpoons \quad H_2CO_3 \text{ (aq)} + OH^- \text{ (aq)}$$

13. Both $Mg(OH)_2$ and $CaCO_3$ are relatively insoluble in water, the solubility product constants, K_{sp}, are small, 1.2×10^{-11} and 8.7×10^{-9}, respectively. Does a small value of K mean that there are more products or more reactants at equilibrium? In other words, is the equilibrium position on the left or on the right?

14. a)   To determine the amount of $Mg(OH)_2$ and $CaCO_3$ in antacids, why can't we do a direct titration with HCl?

    b)   Expla in how back-titration is used to determine the amount of $Mg(OH)_2$ and $CaCO_3$ in antacids.

15. Calculate the volume of 6 M NaOH required to prepare 500 mL of 0.3 M NaOH.

DISCUSSION QUESTIONS

Discuss your results. In standardizing the NaOH solution, were the NaOH concentrations determined within 1.0%? In standardizing the NaOH solution, what was the average NaOH concentration and the deviation? Vinegar is approximately 3% acetic acid by mass. Compare this value with your results. How did the percent composition of active ingredient compare in the two brands of antacids? Were the results obtained accurate? Are you confident in your analysis of percent acetic acid in vinegar and the percent composition of the active ingredients in antacid tablets? Discuss the main sources of error in the experiment.

QUESTIONS

1. If a solution of NaOH is standardized using a sample of KHP which is contaminated with KCl, how would the molarity of NaOH calculated be affected? Would the molarity of NaOH be too high or too low? Explain your answer.

2. a) What volume of 0.4 M HCl is required to neutralize 100.0 mL of 0.3 M LiOH?

   b) What volume of 0.4 M HCl is required to neutralize 100.0 mL of 0.3 M $Mg(OH)_2$?

3. A Rolaids antacid tablet weighed 1.50 g and contained 0.532 g of the active ingredient, $NaAl(OH)_2CO_3$. Assume that the active ingredient reacts with HCl according to the following reaction:

$$NaAl(OH)_2CO_3 + 4\ HCl \quad \rightarrow \quad NaCl + AlCl_3 + 3\ H_2O\ +\ CO_2$$

   How many moles of HCl would one Rolaid tablet neutralize?

4. Determine the number of moles of HCl that can be neutralized by an over the counter antacid tablet that contains 400 mg $Al(OH)_3$.

5. How many acidic hydrogens are there in acetic acid, CH_3COOH? Explain your answer.

Introduction to Kinetics: Factors That Affect the Rate of Reaction

Chad Eller

OBJECTIVES

- Be able to list and rationalize the factors that affect the rates of a reaction.
- Explain various scenarios using the factors that affect reaction kinetics.

INTRODUCTION

Throughout nature, chemical reactions occur at different rates. Some reactions such as the rusting of iron are relatively slow while others such as the combustion of gasoline occur very quickly. Scientists, however, have figured out ways to make various reactions run faster or slower. Becoming familiar with the factors that affect the rate of a reaction gives us insight into how reactions work. The field of chemistry that is concerned with the rate at which reactions occur is called chemical kinetics.

A rough analogy can be made to the speed with which a computer completes a specific task. All computers are not created equal. If you try to run the newest 3-D game in high resolution on an old machine you'll be lucky to get it to work at all. Each component of a computer has a definite and predictable effect on its performance. Too little RAM, slow bus speed, fragmented hard drive, inefficient operating system or application, multitasking, network congestion – they all work to slow down our computing experience. But for each problem there is a solution. It just takes a little knowledge (theory) and a few tries at improvement (experiments).

Chemists and computer engineers are not the only people concerned with the rates of processes. Consider these examples:

Career	Application
Biologist	Preservation or decomposition of specimens
Chemical Engineer	Speed of production effecting cost
Civil Engineer	Concrete and asphalt curing
Doctor	Medication or poison effecting the body
Museum Curator	Dating, restoration, preservation of artifacts
Restaurant Owner	Food spoilage and safety

BACKGROUND

In order to understand each factor that affects the rate of a chemical reaction we can use the simple model of atoms as very small spheres in constant motion. Molecules are groups of these spheres that are bonded together and are constantly bouncing off each other. Picture just a few molecules at a time and consider what happens to them in different circumstances. Think of this model as we study the effects of concentration, surface area (for solids), temperature, and catalysts.

Effect of Changing the Concentration of Reactants

Chemical reactions involve breaking chemical bonds, rearranging the reactant atoms, and making new chemical bonds. In order for this to occur, molecules must collide with each other. If there are only a few molecules of each reactant in a given volume, the number of collisions between them will be relatively low. By increasing the concentration of the reactants, we increase the number of reactant molecules in the same amount of space. This means there are more opportunities for a collision to occur.

Fishing can be used as an analogy for the effect of concentration. If you are fishing in a well-stocked pond with thousands of fish (a high concentration) you have a better chance of catching a fish than if the same pond only had 2 or 3 fish (a lower concentration).

Effect of Changing the Surface Area

In the case where one of the reactants is a solid, the majority of the atoms are trapped beneath the surface. Only the atoms on the surface are available to collide with the other reactant. When a sample cube is cut into smaller pieces (Figure 1), the amount of surface area increases, even though the volume does not change. Grinding a solid into a powder vastly increases the surface area, making a larger portion of the atoms available to collide with the other reactant. In your daily experience, you may have seen that fine salt crystals dissolve in water faster than course rock salt.

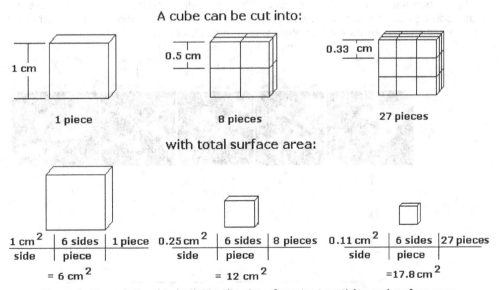

A cube can be cut into:

1 cm — 1 piece   0.5 cm — 8 pieces   0.33 cm — 27 pieces

with total surface area:

$$\frac{1\,cm^2}{side} \mid \frac{6\,sides}{piece} \mid 1\,piece \qquad \frac{0.25\,cm^2}{side} \mid \frac{6\,sides}{piece} \mid 8\,pieces \qquad \frac{0.11\,cm^2}{side} \mid \frac{6\,sides}{piece} \mid 27\,pieces$$

$$= 6\,cm^2 \qquad\qquad = 12\,cm^2 \qquad\qquad = 17.8\,cm^2$$

Figure 1. The relationship between the size of reactant particles and surface area

Effect of Changing the Temperature

The average molecular kinetic energy of a sample is constant at a given temperature. However, the random nature of molecular motion means that some molecules will be moving faster than others. At any given temperature a few molecules have enough energy to react. This minimum required energy is called the activation energy, E_a. As the temperature of the system is increased, the kinetic energy available during collisions goes up and the proportion of collisions exceeding E_a increases (Figure 2). This allows the reaction to take place faster at a higher temperature.

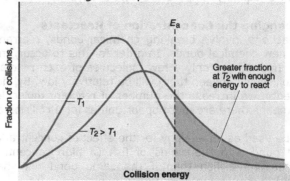

Figure 2. The relationship between temperature and
the fraction of collisions with enough energy to react

Think of rolling a ball up an inclined driveway into a garage. If you roll the ball slowly, it comes right back to you. When you roll it fast enough, however, the ball makes it into the garage. The amount of energy needed to get the ball into the garage is analogous to the activation energy of a reaction. Only when a molecule can acquire at least that much energy does a reaction take place.

Just as some driveways are steeper than others, chemical reactions differ in the amount of energy needed to make them occur. Why don't all reactions have the same E_a? Sometimes the bond to be broken is very strong. In other reactions there is an unstable intermediate molecule that requires a lot of energy to make (Figure 3).

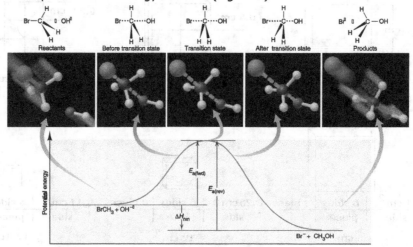

Figure 3. Activation energy and transition state for the reaction between CH_3Br and OH^-

Orientation of the Collisions

As every baseball player knows, hitting the ball does not guarantee a home run. Sometimes the ball hits the top of the bat and pops straight up, other times it hits the bottom of the bat, and the batter grounds out. Only when the swing is perfectly aligned with the ball can you hit a home run.

Likewise, in chemistry, every collision does not result in a chemical reaction (Figure 4). In order for bonds to form, atomic orbitals must overlap just right. Complex molecules can have shapes that make it unlikely for this overlapping of orbitals to happen in any particular collision. The likelihood of a correct spatial relationship is expressed in the constant 'A', which we will use later in a mathematical model of reaction rates.

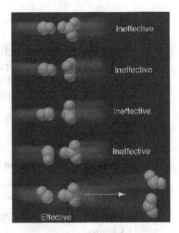

Figure 4. The importance of correct collision orientation on the success of a chemical reaction.

Effect of Adding a Catalyst

Although scientists are not able to directly control the activation energy or the orientation of a collision for a reaction, the use of catalysts often allow for the manipulation of these factors. A catalyst is a material that does not permanently change or get used up in a reaction, but helps the reaction run faster. The catalyst lets a reaction form the same product it normally would, but by following a different, less energy intensive route (Figure 5).

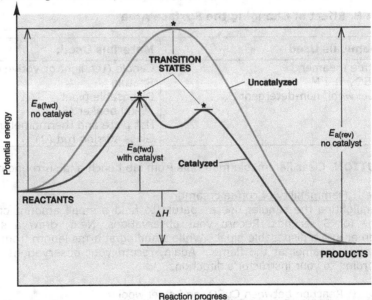

Figure 5. The difference in activation energy between a catalyzed and uncatalyzed reaction.

You can think of catalysts as bridges: they let you cross a river without having to walk miles and miles to find a shallow spot to wade across. Bridges are used, but not destroyed, and where you end up is the same. They just make the trip easier and faster. Catalysts work in many different and often complicated ways. Sometimes they temporarily donate or absorb electrons, hydrogen ions or hydroxide ions in order to provide the alternative, lower energy reaction mechanism.

OVERVIEW

Each factor that affects the rate of reaction will be demonstrated with a chemical reaction or model. Pay attention to which factor is affecting the rate in each case. A key to understanding kinetics is to consider how the changes we make will determine what the atoms are experiencing thereby leading to a change in the rate of reaction.

PROCEDURE

Part A. Effect of Changing the Concentration of Reactants

Chemicals Used	Materials Used:
HCl, 1M and 6M in dropper bottles Chalk	Watch glass (2)

CAUTION: 6M HCl is caustic. If any is spilled on your skin, immediately rinse with running water and inform your laboratory instructor. As always, you should wear your goggles at all times when working in the laboratory. Dispose of waste according to instructor's directions.

Place a small piece of chalk in each of the two watch glasses. Add 10 drops of 1M HCl to one sample of chalk and 6M HCl on the other. Record your observations.

Part B. Effect of Changing the Surface Area

Chemicals Used	Materials Used:
Coffee creamer $CuSO_4$, 0.2 M Steel wool, non-detergent	Candle (tea light or votive candle) and lighter Spatula Disposable pipet 50-ml beaker (3) Hot plate and thermometer Glass stirring rod (2)

CAUTION: Clear flammable materials from lab bench and surrounding areas.

Case I: Flammability of coffee creamer
After lighting the candle, use a spatula to hold a small amount of coffee creamer in the flame for 5 seconds. Record your observations. Next, draw a small amount of coffee creamer into a disposable pipet. While standing at arms length from the candle, aim a burst of coffee creamer at the flame. Again, record your observations. Clean your lab bench according to your instructor's directions.

Case II: Reaction between $CuSO_4$ and steel wool
Add 25 mL of 0.2 M $CuSO_4$ to each of two 50-mL beakers and heat both to 80°C. While the solution is heating, prepare two pieces of steel wool. Each piece should be about 0.2 grams. The first piece should be stretched out and the second piece should be rolled between your fingers until it becomes a tight ball. Simultaneously drop the pieces of steel wool into the two beakers and stir. Record any color changes and how long it took before the changes occurred. Dispose of waste according to your instructor's directions.

Part C. Effect of Changing the Temperature

Chemicals Used	Materials Used:
Food coloring (dark) $CuSO_4$ (0.2 M) Ice Zinc metal (10 mesh, granular)	400-mL beaker (2) Hot plate and thermometer Tongs or heat resistant gloves Spatula 50-mL beaker (3) 100-mL beaker Clay, small lump

Case I: Dispersal of dye in hot and cold water
Fill two 400-mL beakers each with 250 mL water. Heat one to 80°C. Without stirring, add one drop of food coloring to each container by touching the surface with the dropper. Record the time required for the color to disperse.

Case II: Reaction between $CuSO_4$ and zinc
Add 25 mL of 0.2 M $CuSO_4$ to each of two 50-mL beakers. Heat one solution to 80°C, while cooling the other in an ice bath. Add a few pieces of granular zinc to the cold container. Record any color changes and how long it took for the changes to occur. Repeat by adding a few pieces of zinc to the hot solution. Again, record your results. Dispose of waste according to your instructor's directions.

Case III: Modeling Activation Energy
Roll a piece of modeling clay into a ball no bigger than a ping-pong ball. Drop the clay on a clean area of floor from a height of 1 foot. Gently push the clay sideways to see if it rolls. Note any shape change upon impact. Drop the clay several more times each time about one foot higher. Roughly how high did you need to drop the clay for it to stick firmly to the floor?

Part D. Modeling the Significance of the Orientation of Collisions

Materials Used:
Styrofoam-Velcro balls (4, 2 each with one piece of Velcro and 2 each with 6 pieces of Velcro) Box or deep tray

Place two of the Styrofoam balls with 6 pieces of Velcro on them in a box or deep tray. Gently shake the container until the two balls stick. Repeat with the 2 balls that have only one Velcro square. Describe how readily the balls stick together in each case.

Part E. Effect of Adding a Catalyst

Chemicals Used	Materials Used:
Hydrogen peroxide (H_2O_2), 6% solution KI Ice 0.5% corn starch solution Iodine solution (saturated) in dropper bottles	100-mL beaker Hot plate and thermometer Tongs or heat resistant gloves 600-mL beaker Spatula 50-mL beaker (3) Glass stirring rod (2)

CAUTION: Avoid contact with hydrogen peroxide. If any is spilled on your skin, immediately rinse with running water and inform your laboratory instructor. As always, wear your goggles at all times when working in the laboratory. Dispose of peroxide waste according to instructor's directions. In general, peroxide waste is NOT compatible with other chemical waste.

Case I: Decomposing H_2O_2

In a 100-mL beaker, heat 20 ml of 6% H_2O_2 to 80°C. Using tongs or heat resistant gloves, remove the beaker from the hot plate and place the whole beaker inside a large 600-mL beaker. Using a spatula, add roughly 0.05 g of KI (a pinky nail sized portion) to the H_2O_2. Record your observations. Do not view from above, as minor splashing may occur. After 30 - 45 seconds, add 10 mL of ice to the solution. Again, record your observations.

Case II: Hydrolysis of Starch

Using 50-mL beakers, warm two, 10-mL samples of 0.5 % corn starch solution to 40°C. Add 10 drops of iodine to each sample and record your observations. Collect 2 mL of saliva from yourself and lab partner. Thoroughly mix the saliva into one of the corn starch/iodine solutions. Record the time required for the solution to become light lavender or clear. Add a few more drops of iodine. Note the color of drops as they enter solution, and the color after mixing. Dispose of waste according to your instructor's directions.

Introduction to Kinetics: Factors That Affect the Rate of Reaction

Name:	Lab Instructor:
Date:	Lab Section:

PRE-LABORATORY EXERCISES

1. Name four factors that are under the control of a scientist when he or she wants to increase the rate of a reaction.

2. As scientists, we often talk about wanting to speed reactions up. Can you think, however, of any reactions that you might rather slow down than speed up? Can you imagine any way to use the factors from the previous question to help you control the specific reaction you want to slow down?

3. You have an important project due tomorrow and you are trying to use every free second to put on the finishing touches. Whenever possible, you also rush through your typical daily tasks and responsibilities. Which of the following has associated with it a time constraint that is under your control and can be adjusted safely: showering, driving to school, math class, eating lunch, Doctor's appointment and grocery shopping. Briefly explain your answers.

4. A living cell must accomplish many complicated chemical tasks. Our bodies contain countless enzymes that are used to speed up otherwise slow reactions. Knowing that enzymes are a type of catalyst, which of the following factors is effected by the presence of an enzyme: the energy of the reactants, the energy of the products, the energy of the transition state, the likelihood of a collision with the correct orientation, or the temperature of the reaction. Briefly explain your answer(s).

Introduction to Kinetics: Factors That Affect the Rate of Reaction

Name:	Lab Instructor:
Date:	Lab Section:

RESULTS and POST-LABORATORY QUESTIONS

Part A. Effect of Changing the Concentration of Reactants
In what ways was the reaction between the chalk and the 1 M HCl similar to the reaction between the chalk and the 6 M HCl? In what ways were the reactions different?

Part B. Effect of Changing the Surface Area
Case I: Flammability of coffee creamer
What was the effect of spraying the coffee creamer at the flame rather than holding a spatula full in the flame? Explain your observations in terms of surface area.

Case II: Reaction between $CuSO_4$ and steel wool
Describe the appearance of the solution before addition of the steel wool.

Describe the appearance of the solution and the steel wool after the reaction.

In which case did the reaction occur first? Explain why.

Part C. Effect of Changing the Temperature
Case I: Dispersal of dye in hot and cold water
Time required to disperse dye in room temperature water:
Time required to disperse dye in hot water:
Explain your observations in terms of the kinetic energy of the water molecules.

OVER →

RESULTS and POST-LABORATORY QUESTIONS continued...

Case II: Reaction between $CuSO_4$ and zinc

	Cold Solution	Hot Solution
Time for 1st color change in the...		
Time for 2nd color change in the...		

What effect does increasing the temperature have on the rate of reaction? Explain why.

Case III: Modeling Activation Energy
Why doesn't the clay always stick to the floor? Explain how this activity serves as an analogy for activation energy.

Part D. Modeling the Significance of the Orientation of Collisions
In which case (the ball with 1 Velcro or 6 Velcro pieces) was the required orientation for successful collision more restrictive? Explain.

Did this agree with your observations of how long it took for the balls to stick? Explain.

Part E. Effect of Adding a Catalyst
Case I: Decomposing H_2O_2
Observations after addition of KI:

Observations after addition of ice:

In Case I, which material is the catalyst?

Does temperature affect the usefulness of a catalyst?

RESULTS and POST-LABORATORY QUESTIONS continued...

Case II: Hydrolysis of Starch
Description of corn starch solution:

Observation after addition of Iodine:

Observation after addition of saliva (compare with control):

Observation after addition of more Iodine:

1. Marble, like chalk is composed of $CaCO_3$. Explain why monitoring the acidity of rainfall would be important with regards to conserving historically and artistically important outdoor statues.

2. A chemical engineer is trying to increase output of a chemical plant. She is considering using an expensive catalyst or increasing the temperature of the large reaction vessel by 20°C to accomplish the same task. Which route will be least expensive in the short term? Long term?

3. Is the blue chemical in the $CuSO_4$ solution a catalyst? How do you know?

4. As a reaction progresses and the reactants are consumed, will this tend to increase or decrease the rate of reaction? Explain.

Determining the Rate Law: A Kinetics Study of the Iodination of Acetone

Kristen Spotz

OBJECTIVES

- Gain a quantitative understanding of kinetics.
- Determine the rate of a reaction, the order of the reaction with respect to the reactants and the value of the rate constant.
- Predict reaction times using an experimentally determined rate law.

INTRODUCTION

One factor influencing the rate of a reaction is the concentration of the reactants. Typically, as the concentration of reactants increases so does the rate of a reaction. The actual relationship, however, can be quite complicated. Sometimes, doubling the concentration will result in a doubling of the rate. For other chemical reactions, however, doubling the concentration of a reactant might have no effect on the rate or it might result in a four-fold increase in the rate. It can be extremely useful for a scientist to have an understanding of the relationship between the concentration of the reactants and the rate of the reaction. For example, with a quantitative knowledge of reaction rates, scientists are able to gain insight into reaction mechanisms and even predict the time frame of a reaction. Detailed studies by 1995 Nobel laureates F. Sherwood Rowland and Mario Molina of the rates of hundreds of chemical reactions provided insight into the role of chlorfluorocarbons (CFCs) in the depletion of the ozone layer. So, how do scientists determine the relationship between concentration and reaction rate and how are the results expressed in a useful form?

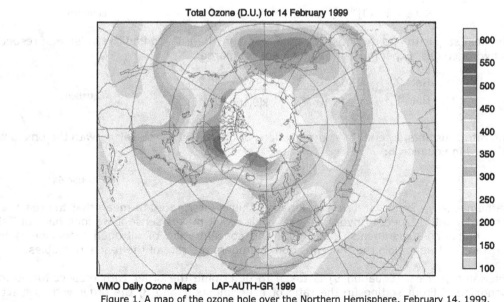

Total Ozone (D.U.) for 14 February 1999

WMO Daily Ozone Maps   LAP-AUTH-GR 1999

Figure 1. A map of the ozone hole over the Northern Hemisphere, February 14, 1999.
World Meteorological Organization: www.wmo.ch/web/arep/nhoz/html.

BACKGROUND

The Rate Law

All the information needed to predict the rate of a given reaction is contained in the rate law, or the rate equation. Given the generic reaction in Equation 1, the general form of the rate law would be given in Equation 2:

$$aA + bB \rightarrow cC + dD \qquad \text{Equation 1}$$

$$\text{rate} = k[A]^m[B]^n \qquad \text{Equation 2}$$

The rate constant, k, is specific for each reaction and is temperature dependent. The units for k are dependent on the overall order of the reaction. The rate law also includes the concentrations of the reactants raised to the reaction orders, m and n. The values for m and n must be determined experimentally (as you will do in today's experiment) and cannot be derived from the balanced chemical equation.

As an example, we will examine the reaction (Equation 3) and the experimental data (Table 1) for the reaction of nitrogen monoxide and hydrogen gas to produce nitrogen gas and steam.

$$2NO\ (g) + 2H_2\ (g) \rightarrow N_2\ (g) + 2H_2O\ (g) \qquad \text{Equation 3}$$

Exp. #	$[NO]_{initial}$, M	$[H_2]_{initial}$, M	Initial rate, M/s	Table 1
1	0.10	0.10	1.23×10^{-3}	
2	0.10	0.20	2.46×10^{-3}	
3	0.20	0.10	4.92×10^{-3}	

The first step in determining the rate law is to follow the example in Equation 2 and write the general form of the rate law for the reaction (Equation 4):

$$\text{Rate} = k[NO]^m[H_2]^n \qquad \text{Equation 4}$$

The next step is to find the order for each reactant. In order to find the order with respect to hydrogen gas, Experiment #1 and #2 are compared:

$$\frac{\text{Rate 2}}{\text{Rate 1}} = \frac{2.46 \times 10^{-3}}{1.23 \times 10^{-3}} = \frac{k[0.10]^m[0.20]^n}{k[0.10]^m[0.10]^n} \qquad \text{Equation 5}$$

The rate constants, k, and the concentrations of nitrite will cancel (along with the unknown m) leaving Equation 6:

$$2 = 2^n \qquad \text{Equation 6}$$

Mathematically, $n = 1$. In terms of kinetics, this is interpreted to mean that the reaction is first order with respect to hydrogen gas. This result makes sense if we look back at Table 1. Comparing experiments 1 and 2, if the concentration of nitrogen monoxide is held constant and we double the concentration hydrogen, the rate of the reaction doubles.

The same process (Equation 5) is taken to determine the order with respect to nitrogen monoxide.   From setting up the ratio of experiments 1 and 3, the order with respect to nitrogen monoxide is determined to be second order. This means that if the concentration of hydrogen is held constant while doubling the concentration of nitrogen monoxide, the rate of the overall reaction quadruples. The overall order of the reaction (n+m) is 3.

Now that we know the order of the reaction, the next step is to determine the value of the rate constant, k. The units for k are dependent on the overall order of the reaction. Data from any experiment given in the table may be used to determine the rate constant. For example, using the data from experiment #1 results in Equation 7.

$$1.23 \times 10^{-3} \text{ M/s} = k[0.10 \text{ M}][0.10 \text{ M}]^2 \qquad \text{Equation 7}$$

Solving for the rate constant, the value is equal to $1.23 \text{ M}^{-2}\text{s}^{-1}$. The final rate law includes the value for both the rate constant and the orders of the reaction.

$$\text{Rate} = 1.23 \text{ M}^{-2}\text{s}^{-1} [H_2][NO]^2 \qquad \text{Equation 8}$$

Using Equation 8 above, any initial concentration of hydrogen gas and nitrogen monoxide can be inserted into the rate law in order to predict the rate of the reaction.

The Iodination of Acetone

In today's experiment, you will be studying the kinetics of the reaction between acetone and iodine to form iodoacetone and iodide (Equation 9).

$$CH_3COCH_3 \text{ (aq)} + I_2 \text{ (aq)} \rightarrow CH_3COCH_2I \text{ (aq)} + H^+ \text{ (aq)} + I^- \text{ (aq)} \qquad \text{Equation 9}$$
$$\text{yellow} \qquad\qquad\qquad\qquad\qquad\qquad \text{colorless}$$

The rate law will be determined by varying the concentration of acetone and iodine. To study reaction rates it is necessary to measure the concentration of reactants as a function of time at the start of the reaction (the "initial rate" in Table 1), making kinetic studies typically difficult. In this particular experiment, however, the amount of acetone will be kept in vast excess with respect to the amount of iodine so that the concentration of acetone does not change appreciably during the course of the reaction. As a result, the rate of the reaction remains relatively constant throughout the course of the reaction. In other words, the "initial rate" that we need in order to determine the rate law will be equated with the average rate of the reaction. The equation used to find the average rate of reaction (Equation 10) is found by measuring the change in iodine concentration divided by the time needed to react.

$$\text{Rate} = \frac{-\Delta[I_2]}{\Delta t} = \frac{-([I_2]_{final} - [I_2]_{initial})}{\Delta t} \qquad \text{Equation 10}$$

The study of the reaction for the iodination of acetone is also made easy due to the color changes of the solution. Iodine (I_2) is a pale yellow whereas the iodide ion (I^-) is colorless. Hydrochloric acid, which is introduced to the reactant solution as a catalyst, is also colorless. Therefore, changes in iodine concentration can easily be visualized. The time at which the pale yellow color of the initial solution turns clear indicates that the reaction is complete and that $[I_2]_{final} = 0$ M.

OVERVIEW

After following a procedure for the preparation of Solution 1, you will devise your own experimental protocol for creating Solutions 2,3, and 4 in order to determine the order with respect to acetone and iodine, the value of the rate constant, and predictions concerning reaction rate.

PROCEDURE: Students work in pairs

Chemicals Used	Materials Used
4 M Acetone (100 mL)	50-mL Graduated cylinders (4)
1 M HCl (100 mL)	100-mL Beakers (4)
0.00118 M Iodine (100 mL)	125-mL Erlenmeyer flasks (5)
De-ionized water (DI H$_2$O)	Plastic pipet (4)
	Stop-watch
	Stir-plate and stir bar (optional)

1. Thoroughly clean four 100-mL beakers, four 50-mL graduated cylinders and five 125-mL Erlenmeyer flasks with soap and water. Rinse all the glassware with de-ionized water and allow to dry. Label one of each beaker and graduated cylinder with the following: "acetone", "HCl", "I$_2$", "DI H$_2$O". Label four of the Erlenmeyer flasks with numbers 1 – 4 and label the last flask "blank". Rinse each beaker/graduated cylinder with 2-3 mLs of the solution named on the label. Pour approximately 50 mL of the appropriate solution into the labeled 100-mL beakers.

2. Prepare a blank that you will use for a color comparison. The blank should consist of 50-mL of water in a 125-mL Erlenmeyer flask.

3. With the appropriately labeled 50-mL graduated cylinders, add 10.0 mL of acetone, 10.0 mL of HCl and 20.0 mL of de-ionized water into a clean 125-mL Erlenmeyer flask (labeled Solution #1).

4. Measure 10.0 mL of 0.00118 M iodine into the clean "I$_2$" graduated cylinder. Place the Erlenmeyer flask (Solution 1) onto the stir-plate and drop a stir bar into the solution. Set the stir plate to a medium setting. Quickly pour all the iodine solution into the Erlenmeyer flask. Immediately begin timing the reaction as soon as all the iodine has been transferred to Solution #1. The solution will appear yellow due to the presence of iodine. The color will fade as the iodine reacts with the acetone. Record the time when the color of iodine just disappears by comparison with the blank. Record the volumes of acetone, HCl, iodine and H$_2$O for Solution #1.

5. Repeat steps 3 and 4. Calculate and record the percent difference between the two times. Repeat until the percent difference is less than 5%.

6. With your partner, decide how to alter the composition of Solution #1 to determine the order with respect to iodine (Solution #2) and the order with respect to acetone (Solution #3). The only requirement is that you must maintain a total volume of 50 mL and the volume of HCl must be 10 mL. After showing your proposal to your instructor, carry out the reactions for Solutions 2 and 3 exactly as described for Solution #1.

7. For your final reaction, devise Solution #4 using reactant volumes that you have not previously used. Remember, the total volume must remain 50 mL and that 10 mL of the total volume must be 1 M HCl. Record the time of the reaction.

Determining the Rate Law: A Kinetics Study of the Iodination of Acetone

Name:	Lab Instructor:
Date:	Lab Section:

PRE-LABORATORY EXERCISES

1. According to your textbook, what are the four factors that affect the rate of a chemical reaction? Which of these factors will be studied in this experiment?

2. Distinguish among the following terms: initial rate, average rate, and instantaneous rate.

   Which of these rates would you expect to have the largest value? Explain.

   Which of the rates are typically used to determine the rate law for a reaction?

   Which of these rates will we use to determine the rate law for a reaction?

3. Use Equation 9 to predict the initial rate if $[NO]_{initial} = 0.30$ M and $[H_2]_{initial} = 0.15$ M.

   What would happen to the initial rate of the reaction if $[NO]_{initial} = 0.60$ M and $[H_2]_{initial} = 0.15$ M instead. Does your result make sense in terms of the order of the reaction?

OVER →

PRE-LABORATORY EXERCISES continued...

4. Assuming that concentrations are expressed in moles per liter and time in seconds, what are the units of the rate constant, k, for an overall first order rate law? Show your work.

What are the units of k for an overall second order rate law? Show your work.

Using these two rate constants as examples, write a general rule to explain how the units of the rate constant depend on the overall order of the rate law.

5. Write the general form of the rate law for the reaction in Equation 9.

Determining the Rate Law: A Kinetics Study of the Iodination of Acetone

Name:	Lab Instructor:
Date:	Lab Section:

RESULTS and POST-LABORATORY QUESTIONS

	Solution #1	Solution #2	Solution #3	Solution #4
Volume, 4.0 M acetone				
Volume, 1 M HCl				
Volume, H_2O				
Volume, 0.00118 M iodine				
Reaction time, Trial 1 *				
Reaction time, Trial 2 *				
Average reaction time				

* For Solution #1, only record the times for the two trials within 5%.

Summarize your results as in Table 1 in the BACKGROUND:

Solution #	[acetone]$_{initial}$, M ##	[iodine]$_{initial}$, M ##	Initial rate, M/s **
1			
2			
3			
4			

Be sure to account for your dilution to 50 mLs.
** Use Equation 10 in BACKGROUND.

1. Determine the rate law (including the values for the orders of the reaction and the value for the rate constant with units) for the reaction studied in this experiment. Show all your work.

2. Use the rate law to make a prediction for the theoretical initial rate of the reaction for Solution #4. How does it compare to the experimental initial rate for Solution #4?

OVER →

RESULTS and POST-LABORATORY QUESTIONS continued...

3. Why is it important to keep the total volume of Solutions #1-4 at 50 mLs? If more water had been introduced to one of the solutions (giving a total volume of 60 mLs), would you expect the reaction rate to increase or decrease? Explain.

4. The following reaction occurs without a change in the color. $2A\,(g) + B_2\,(g) \rightarrow 2AB\,(g)$
   a) How could you monitor the concentration of the reactants and products?

   b) How would you determine the reaction orders?

   c) How would you find the rate constant and the units for the rate constant?

Spectrophotometric Analysis: Phosphates in Water

Kristen Spotz

OBJECTIVES

- Practice calculating and performing dilutions of solutions.
- Determine the concentration of phosphate in a water sample by spectrophotometric analysis.
- Construct and utilize a calibration curve.
- Explore the dynamics of working with a larger group of students.

INTRODUCTION

Imagine a time when the lakes and rivers are no longer safe for swimming or boating, or when the ocean is no longer a source of food. Coastal zones and estuaries, some of the most productive ecosystems in the world, are in danger. The problem of eutrophication, is affecting the water supply of towns across the nation making the water unsafe for consumption and hazardous to the wildlife that depend upon it.

The source of the eutrophication problem is an excessive input of nutrients into rivers, lakes and the seas because of the extensive use of fertilizers, the combustion of fossil fuels and waste from animal feedlots. This excessive nutrient input stimulates the growth of algae and bacteria, robbing the water of precious oxygen. The resulting algal blooms, red tides and deterioration of sea grass makes the waters uninhabitable for most fish and coastal wildlife.

What role will you play as a future scientist or citizen in ensuring the protection of our valuable water resource?

BACKGROUND

Phosphates are one of the major groups of contaminates affecting our nation's water supply. Phosphates are found in the environment, not only in the form you have seen in your chemistry book (PO_4^{3-}), but also as polyphosphates (such as $P_2O_7^{4-}$ or $P_3O_{10}^{5-}$) or as organic phosphates which are eventually <u>hydrolyzed</u> to form PO_4^{3-}. The primary means by which humans introduce phosphates into the environment is through the use of fertilizers and detergents. In particular, tripolyphosphates ($P_3O_{10}^{5-}$) have been used in soaps and detergents to combat the problem of hard water. Phosphates are also a major component of fertilizers, because phosphorus is a necessary plant nutrient and is crucial for seed formation, root development, and crop maturation. These phosphates eventually enter the water supply leaving lakes, rivers, and seas with an abnormally high phosphate concentration.

Spectrophotometric Analysis and the Determination of Phosphate

Spectrophotometric analysis relies on the fact that the amount of light absorbed by a sample shows a linear dependence upon the concentration of the compound present in the solution. You have probably seen this phenomenon for yourself before. Just hold up two glasses of juice made from powdered concentrate; one made with three scoops and one made with one scoop. The more concentrated drink absorbs more light and is darker. The problem with using spectrophotometric analysis in our case is that phosphates are colorless and therefore do not absorb light in the visible portion of the <u>electromagnetic spectrum</u>. However, due to the reactive nature of phosphates, one can easily color them using an ammonium vanadomolybdate reagent. This reagent includes ammonium metavanadate (NH_4VO_3) and molybdate (MoO_4^{2-}) and reacts with the phosphate to form a yellow compound (called "heteropoly acid" from here on). The formula of the yellow compound is uncertain but thought to be $(NH_4)_3PO_4 \cdot NH_4VO_3 \cdot 16MoO_3$. The brightness of the resulting yellow solution is directly proportional to the concentration of phosphate in the water.

Scientists use an instrument called a spectrometer to quantitatively determine the amount of light absorbed by a solution. The primary inner parts of a typical spectrometer are illustrated in Figure 1. The spectrometer has a light source that emits light which is focused with a small slit. The wavelength of interest is then selected using the monochrometer ("mono" meaning one and "chromate" meaning color) and an additional slit. The selected light then reaches the sample and depending on how the photons interact with the compound of interest, the light is either absorbed or passes straight through. By comparing the amount of light entering the sample (P_o) with the amount of light reaching the detector (P), the spectrometer is able to tell how much light is absorbed.

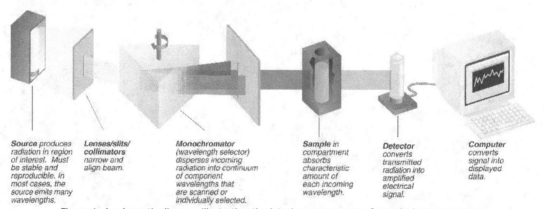

Source produces radiation in region of interest. Must be stable and reproducible. In most cases, the source emits many wavelengths.

Lenses/slits/ collimators narrow and align beam.

Monochromator (wavelength selector) disperses incoming radiation into continuum of component wavelengths that are scanned or individually selected.

Sample in compartment absorbs characteristic amount of each incoming wavelength.

Detector converts transmitted radiation into amplified electrical signal.

Computer converts signal into displayed data.

Figure 1. A schematic diagram illustrating the interior components of a typical spectrometer.

Scientists quantify the amount of light passing through the sample in terms of percent transmittance (%T). Percent transmittance is calculated as the fraction of original light that passes through a sample (Equation 1).

$$\% T = \left(\frac{P}{P_0}\right) \times 100 \qquad \text{Equation 1}$$

Equation 2 shows how percent transmittance (%T) can easily be converted into a quantity known as absorbance (A). Though most spectrophotometers give readings in terms of both %T and A, measurements should be made in %T and mathematically converted to A because %T can be determined more accurately.

$$A = -\log\left(\frac{\%T}{100}\right) \qquad \text{Equation 2}$$

The absorbance of a sample is important because of the previously mentioned linear relationship between absorbance the concentration of the sample. This relationship is known as Beer's law (Equation 3).

$$A = \varepsilon bc \qquad \text{Equation 3}$$

The amount of the light that is absorbed depends on several variables:

- "A" is the absorbance of the sample, which in this experiment is due to the interaction of phosphate, in the form of heteropoly acid, with the photons of light. Although the compound being studied may, in general, absorb light over a fairly broad range of wavelengths, there is only one region where the light is absorbed most strongly. This wavelength is known as λ_{max} (pronounced "lambda max"). The absorbance of the sample should be measured at this wavelength.

- "ε" is the molar absorptivity. The molar absorptivity is a constant representing the efficiency by which the substance absorbs light. The greater the value of "ε" the more strongly the substance absorbs light resulting in a more intense color.

- "b" represents the solution path length. It is the distance that the light must travel through the sample and is measured as the width of the sample holder (also called a cuvette). "b" is a constant for each experiment (typically 1 cm).

- "c" represents the molar concentration of the absorbing species in the sample.

One can easily determine the unknown concentration of a sample from Equation 3 after measuring the absorbance of the sample and using the molar absorptivity of the compound and the path length of the cuvette. If the molar absorptivity of the compound is not known, the concentration of an unknown can still be found by constructing a calibration curve.

The Calibration Curve

A calibration curve allows scientists to determine the unknown concentration of a known species. According to Beer's law, as long as we account for a blank solution in our studies, a plot of absorbance versus concentration gives a straight line with slope = "εb" and a y-intercept = 0. For example, the calibration curve in Figure 3 is used to determine the concentration of an unknown solution of iron. The graph is constructed from six points that are made from a stock solution of iron having a known concentration. The experimentally measured absorbance of each of the six solutions is then plotted as a function of concentration and a line of best fit is drawn through the points. As expected, the absorbance of the sample increases linearly as the concentration increases. The absorbance value of 0.357 was then measured for the unknown iron solution of interest. To relate the absorbance to the unknown concentration we can either use the equation of the line of best fit or we can extrapolate from the graph (as shown in Figure 2). This absorbance value was found to correspond to a concentration of 3.59 M of iron in the unknown sample.

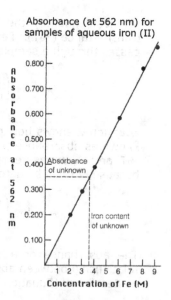

Absorbance (at 562 nm) for samples of aqueous iron (II)

Figure 2. A sample calibration curve used to determine the concentration of an unknown sample of ion (II)

The calibration curve in Figure 2 is an example of a successfully constructed graph. The title is labeled above the graph with both the axes clearly labeled using the independent (x-axis) and the dependent (y-axis) variables in the experiment. After plotting each of the data points on the graph, a line of best fit is drawn. Although, the points do not have to fall directly on the line, a good agreement is expected and needed for accurate determination of the concentration of your unknown.

OVERVIEW

In this experiment, students will work in groups to first prepare a series of six standard solutions of known phosphate concentration by dilution of a stock solution. Using λ_{max} of 400nm, the absorbance of the five standard phosphate solutions will be measured and used to construct a calibration curve. The absorbance of a sample of unknown phosphate concentration will then be determined. The calibration curve will be used to relate the absorbance to the unknown concentration of phosphate in the sample.

PROCEDURE

Chemicals Used	Materials Used
Phosphate stock solution (1.00 X 10^{-3} M)	Spectrophotometer
Ammonium vanadomolybdate solution	25-mL Volumetric flask
Various water samples of unknown	1, 5, 10 and 25-mL Pipets and pipet bulb
phosphate concentration	10-mL Cuvette (1 per group of students)
	100-mL Beakers

Part A: Organizing your group

1. Students will work in groups of 2-3 to construct a single calibration curve consisting of 6 data points having phosphate concentrations in the range 4.00×10^{-5} M to 4.00×10^{-4} M. Each student will be responsible for making at least one of the solutions and measuring the absorbance for at least one data point. Show your instructor your calculations for making your 25-mL standard solutions from the 1.00 X 10^{-3} M phosphate stock solution before your group goes on to Part B. Remember, solutions must be made using only the available volumetric flask and pipets.

Part B: Adjusting the Spectrophotometer

2. Turn on the spectrometer (Figure 3) by rotating the power control clockwise. Allow the spectrophotometer to warm-up for five minutes before using.

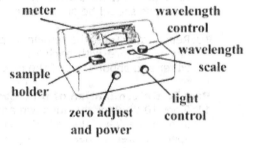

3. Adjust the wavelength to 400 nm. With no sample in the spectrometer, turn the zero adjust so the meter reads 0% T. Each member of the group should verify all readings.

4. Prepare the blank by pipetting 10 mL of de-ionized water and 5 mL of ammonium vanadomolybdate into a beaker.

Figure 3. A typical spectrometer

5. Always rinse the cuvette with a few mLs of solution whenever you are using a new solution. Discard the rinsing solution according to your instructor's directions. Three-quarters fill the rinsed cuvette with the blank solution. Insert the cuvette into the sample holder of the spectrometer and adjust the light-control knob so 100% transmittance is read. Your instrument is now zeroed.

Part C: Preparation of Standard Solutions

6. Based on your calculations from Part A, pipet the appropriate volume of the 1.00 x 10^{-3} M phosphate stock solution into a 25-mL volumetric flask.   Dilute the stock solution by filling the volumetric flask until the meniscus reaches the mark (Figure 4).

7. Pipet 10.0 mL of the phosphate solution you made in step 6 and 5.00 mL of the ammonium vanadomolybdate stock solution into a small, labeled beaker.

8. Repeat steps 6 and 7 for each of the six standard solutions.

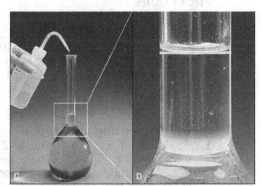

Figure 4: Proper dilution of a solution by filling a volumetric flask to the line

Part D: Making the Calibration Curve Using the Standard Solutions.

9. Rinse the same cuvette you used for your blank with about 1 mL of your standard solution (from step 7). Three-quarters fill the rinsed cuvette with the sample solution. Insert the cuvette into the spectrometer. Measure and record the percent transmittance. All data points for a given curve must be measured with the same cuvette. All phosphate solutions should be discarded according to your instructor's directions.

10. Repeat step 9 for the remaining phosphate solutions that your group made. Before using any glassware with each new solution, the glassware must be rinsed with de-ionized water and about 1 mL of the new solution.

Part E: Determination of Unknown Concentration

11. Pipet 10.0 mL of the unknown and 5.00 mL of the ammonium vanadomolybdate solution into a beaker. Half-fill the rinsed cuvette with the unknown solution. Use the spectrometer to measure the percent transmittance. Record your results.

Before you leave: Make sure everyone in your group has recorded the concentration and the %T for each of the various phosphate solutions.

Spectrophotometric Analysis: Phosphates in Water

Name:	Lab Instructor:
Date:	Lab Section:

PRE-LABORATORY EXCERCISES

1. Define the <u>underlined</u> words in the BACKGROUND section.

2. In your own words, summarize the purpose of a calibration curve.

3. To prepare yourself for performing the dilutions required in this laboratory experiment, read the section on dilutions in your textbook. What volume of 1.00×10^{-3} M phosphate stock solution is required to make 25.0 mL of a 4.00×10^{-5} M solution?

4. Using the spectrophotometer, a sample was analyzed and found to have a percent transmittance of 85%.
   a) What percent of light was actually absorbed by the sample?

   b) Calculate the absorbance (A) of the sample.

Spectrophotometric Analysis: Phosphates in Water

Name:	Lab Instructor:
Date:	Lab Section:

RESULTS and POST-LABORATORY QUESTIONS

1. Attach a copy of your data table from today's experiment. Your table should include the concentration of phosphate in each standard solution, the measured %T and your calculated absorbance.

2. Attach a copy of your calibration curve. What is the equation of the best-fit line?

3. Determine the concentration of phosphate in your unknown solution by extrapolation of the calibration curve (refer back to Figure 2) and by using the equation for the line of best fit. The extrapolation should be shown on your attached calibration curve. The calculation using the line of best fit should be shown below.

4. The U.S. Public Health Service has set the maximum value of phosphate in the drinking water at 0.30 mg phosphate/liter. Did your unknown water sample violate this standard? Show your work.

6

Thermochemistry

PURPOSE AND LEARNING OBJECTIVES

To develop an understanding of temperature, heat, and heat capacity. To calibrate a simple calorimeter which is used to measure the specific heat of a metal, the heat of solution, and the heat of neutralization.

PRINCIPLES

The first law of thermodynamics states that energy must be conserved. Energy can be converted from one form into another, but can not be created or destroyed. Conservation of energy is as fundamental to chemical processes as the laws of conservation of mass and charge. These laws are not derived but are drawn from an immense number of observations of the way matter behaves. A chemical reaction generally involves breaking bonds and making new bonds. Energy is required to break bonds and energy is released when bonds are formed. In a chemical reaction, if energy is released the reaction is **exothermic** ($\Delta H < 0$) and if energy is absorbed the reaction is **endothermic** ($\Delta H > 0$). In this experiment, the heat of solution will be measured for the dissolution of a salt in aqueous solution and the heat of neutralization will be measured for acid-base reactions.

In a reaction, the energy absorbed or released is in the form of heat. The magnitude of heat flow in a reaction is measured using a thermally insulated container called a **calorimeter**. Ideally, no energy will be lost from the calorimeter to its surroundings. Consider the neutralization reaction for a strong acid reacting with a strong base.

$$H^+ (aq) + OH^- (aq) \rightarrow H_2O (l) + heat$$

The solution and the calorimeter will absorb the heat released by the reaction. The amount of heat absorbed by the solution, q, depends on the mass of the solution, m, its specific heat capacity, c_s, and change in temperature, ΔT.

$$q = m\ c_s\ \Delta T$$

The specific heat capacity is defined as the amount of heat required to raise the temperature of one gram of substance by one degree under constant pressure conditions. The heat released by the reaction is exactly equal to the heat absorbed by the solution and the calorimeter.

$$q_{reaction} = -(q_{solution} + q_{calorimeter})$$

$$q_{reaction} = -(m\ c_s\ \Delta T + C_{cal}\Delta T)$$

where C_{cal} is the heat capacity of the calorimeter in units of $J\ K^{-1}$. In order to calculate the heat of reaction, C_{cal} must be determined. The heat released in a reaction depends on the number of moles of reactant consumed. When two moles of acid react with two moles of base to produce two moles of water, the heat released will be twice as much as when one mole of acid and base is consumed in the reaction.

In this experiment, in addition to measuring heats of reaction, the specific heat capacity of an unknown metal will be determined. The specific and molar heat capacities of a number of metals are shown in Table 1. If the specific heat capacity of an unknown metal is measured, the metal can be identified using the data in this table.

The molar heat capacities are nearly constant for all the metals, with an average value of approximately 25 J mol^{-1} K^{-1}. This was discovered by Pierre Dulong and Alexis Petit in 1819 and is referred to as the **Law of Dulong and Petit**. Even though they did not understand the reason for this, they used this observation to estimate the atomic masses of metals. In 1907 Albert Einstein published a theory explaining the observed molar heat capacities of metals. The metal atoms are treated as oscillators, vibrating in three dimensions. Einstein showed that as the temperature approaches absolute zero (zero degrees Kelvin) the molar heat capacity reduces to 3R, where R is the universal gas constant, R = 8.314 J mol^{-1} K^{-1}. Thus, his theory predicts an average molar heat capacity of 24.9 J mol^{-1} K^{-1}.

Table 1. Specific Heat Capacities and Molar Heat capacities of various metals

Metal	Specific Heat Capacity ($J K^{-1} g^{-1}$)	Molar Heat Capacity ($J mol^{-1} k^{-1}$)
Li	3.561	24.77
Mg	1.024	24.89
Al	0.903	24.35
Fe	0.449	25.10
Ni	0.444	26.07
Zn	0.389	25.40
Cu	0.385	24.44
Ag	0.235	25.35
Au	0.129	25.42
Pb	0.128	26.44

In measuring heat capacities, only differences in temperature are considered. The numerical difference in temperature is the same on the Celsius and Kelvin scales. For example, if the initial temperature is measured to be 20°C and the final temperature 45°C, $\Delta T = 25$°C = 25 K, shown as follows.

$$\Delta T = T_{final} - T_{initial} = 45°C - 20°C = 25°C$$

or

$$\Delta T = T_{final} - T_{initial} = 318 K - 293 K = 25 K$$

The specific heat capacity of water is 4.184 $J°C^{-1}g^{-1}$ or 4.184 $JK^{-1}g^{-1}$. Water has an unusually high heat capacity and boiling point because of a network of hydrogen bonds formed between the water molecules. Thus, a small amount of water can absorb a relatively large amount of heat. As a result, large bodies of water, oceans and lakes, moderate the temperature on earth. It also makes water a convenient coolant for many devices, including engines, vacuum pumps and lasers.

SAFETY
WEAR SAFETY GLASSES

HCl is a strong acid and NaOH is a strong base. In case of contact, rinse thoroughly with water. Clean up spills immediately.

PROCEDURE

This experiment will be performed in pairs. It is important to stay consistent when taking measurements. Have one partner read the thermometer throughout a given part of the lab.

Part 1. The Heat Capacity of the Calorimeter

1. Construct the Styrofoam cup calorimeter shown in Figure 1. Obtain two Styrofoam cups and a lid. Place one cup inside the other and put the lid on.

2. Obtain a 0.1°C thermometer. Be careful using the mercury thermometer. The thermometer runs through the center of a cork, held by a clamp, attached to a ring-stand. Align the thermometer so it goes through the center of the lid, into the cups.

    NOTE: The thermometer must slide easily through the cork, if not, exchange this thermometer for another.

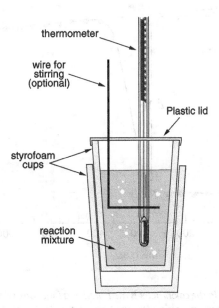

Figure 1. A Styrofoam cup calorimeter.

3. Chill approximately 60 mL of DI water in an ice bath to about 10°C.

4. Heat another 60 mL of DI water to between 60-80°C using a Bunsen burner.

5. Using the 100-mL graduated cylinder, add exactly 50.0 mL of chilled water to the calorimeter. The lid should be on the cup with the thermometer sticking through the lid. Swirl the cup and record the temperature every 30 seconds for 4 minutes, until the temperature is constant. At this point the temperature of the chilled water and the calorimeter have come to equilibrium.

6. When the heated water is between 60-80°C, measure 50.0 mL of the hot water in a graduated cylinder and record its temperature.

7. Quickly add the heated water to the chilled water in the calorimeter.

8. Swirl the cup and begin taking measurements every 15 seconds for 4 minutes. The temperature will rise and then decrease.

Calculate the Heat Capacity of the Calorimeter

1. Use Excel on the computer to graph the temperature of the calorimeter water (°C) on the y-axis and the time (seconds) on the x-axis, as shown in Figure 2.

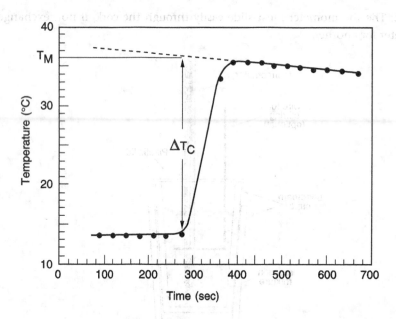

Figure 2. The temperature of the water in the calorimeter is measured as a function of time. Initially the temperature of the cold water is measured. When hot water is added, the temperature is observed to increase. As the hot and cold water mix some heat is lost to the calorimeter so the maximum temperature measured is not as high as it would be if no heat were lost. To obtain the maximum temperature of the solution, T_M, the data must be extrapolated back to the time the solutions were mixed.

2. Determine the maximum temperature, T_M, from your graph.

3. Use the maximum temperature, T_M to calculate the decrease in temperature of the hot water, ΔT_H.

$$\Delta T_H = T_M - T_H$$

4. Use T_M to calculate the increase in temperature of the cold water, ΔT_C.

$$\Delta T_C = T_M - T_C$$

5. The amount of heat lost by the hot water, q_H, is calculated from its mass, m_H, specific heat, c_s, and ΔT_H.

$$q_H = (m_H)(c_s)(\Delta T_H)$$

The specific heat of water, $c_s = 4.184 \text{ J K}^{-1} \text{ g}^{-1}$. The density of water is 1 g/mL.

6. The total amount of heat gained by the cold water and by the calorimeter, q_C, is calculated as the sum of the two.

$$q_C = (m_C)(c_s)(\Delta T_C) + C_{cal}(\Delta T_C)$$

The first quantity represents the heat gained by the cold water in the calorimeter and the second quantity represents the heat gained by the cup, thermometer, and stirrer. The symbol C_{cal} represents the heat capacity of the calorimeter in units of J K^{-1}.

7. The heat gained by the cold water and the calorimeter is exactly equal to heat lost by the hot water.

$$q_C = -q_H$$

$$(m_C)(c_s)(\Delta T_C) + C_{cal}(\Delta T_C) = -(m_H)(c_s)(\Delta T_H)$$

Use this equation, to solve for the heat capacity of the calorimeter, C_{cal}.

8. Repeat the calibration to make sure you are able to obtain consistent results.

9. Show your graphs and calculations to your instructor before proceeding to Part 2.

Part 2. Heat Capacity of an Unknown Metal

1. Fill a 250-mL beaker with approximately 200 mL of DI water. Allow the water to come to room temperature.

2. Set up a Bunsen burner and ring stand with a ring and wire gauze.

3. Weigh a sample of approximately 80 grams of the unknown metal to the nearest 0.01 g. **The metal must be thoroughly dry.** Put the metal sample in a large labeled test tube and loosely stopper the test tube.

4. Fill a 600-mL beaker two thirds full with water.

5. Immerse the test tube in the 600-mL beaker. Heat the water in the beaker to a boil using the Bunsen burner.

6. Once the water is boiling, the test tube must be left for at least 15 minutes to ensure the temperature of the metal reaches equilibrium with the temperature of the water.

7. While keeping an eye on the boiling water, do Part 3.

8. After completing Part 3, clean and dry the calorimeter.

9. Measure 50.0 mL of room temperature DI water.

10. Pour the water into the calorimeter. Stir the water and record the temperature until a consistent temperature is reached.

11. Record the temperature of the boiling water with the test tube containing the metal in it.

12. Using a folded paper towel, take the test tube with the unknown metal out of the boiling water. Quickly and carefully pour the metal into the calorimeter. **Make sure no hot water is added to the calorimeter.**

13. Stir the water in the calorimeter and record the temperature every 30 seconds for about 3 minutes or until the temperature remains constant.

14. Decant most of the water out of the calorimeter. Pour the metal onto a paper towel, dry the metal and put it into the appropriately labeled beaker in the hood. The metal must be completely dry before it can be reused.

Calculate the Heat Capacity of the Unknown Metal and Identify the Metal

1. Use Excel on the computer to graph the temperature of the calorimeter water (°C) on the y-axis and the time (seconds) on the x-axis, analogous to the graph shown in Part 1.

2. Determine T_M and calculate the temperature increase of the water, ΔT_C, and the temperature decrease in the metal, ΔT_H.

3. Using the heat capacity of the calorimeter, C_{cal}, determined in Part 1, calculate the heat gained by the water and the calorimeter.

$$q_C = (m_C)(c_s)(\Delta T_C) + C_{cal}(\Delta T_C)$$

4. The heat lost by the metal equals the heat gained by the water and calorimeter

$$-q_m = q_C$$

$$-(m)(c_{metal})(\Delta T_H) = (m_C)(c_s)(\Delta T_C) + C_{cal}(\Delta T_C)$$

Calculate the specific heat for the unknown metal, c_{metal}. Include units. From the table of specific heats of metals, identify your metal.

5. According to the Law of Dulong and Petit, the molar heat capacity of a metal, c_p, is equal to the specific heat of the metal, c_{metal}, times its molar mass, M.

$$c_p = (c_{metal}) (M)$$

It was shown that $c_p \approx 25 \, JK^{-1}mol^{-1}$ for most metals. Using your experimental value for the specific heat and $c_p = 25 \, JK^{-1}mol^{-1}$, obtain the atomic mass of the unknown metal in the table below.

Specific Heat Capacity of the unknown metal	Metal	Calculated Atomic Mass of the Metal	Actual Atomic Mass of the Metal

Part 3. The Heat of Solution

1. Use the calorimeter calibrated in Part 1. Drain the water and dry the calorimeter.

2. Add 50.0 mL of room temperature DI water to the calorimeter and put on the lid. Let the water sit in the calorimeter 3-4 minutes to allow the water and the calorimeter come to an equilibrium temperature. Record the temperature of the water.

3. Weigh two grams of NH_4NO_3 using weighing paper, to the nearest 0.001 g.

4. Quickly add the ammonium nitrate to the calorimeter. Swirl the cup and record the temperature every 15 seconds for 5 minutes.

5. Drain the ammonium nitrate solution from the calorimeter into the appropriately labeled waste bottle in the hood. Rinse the calorimeter with DI water and dry it.

Calculate the Heat of Solution

1. Write the balanced equation for the reaction.

2. Use Excel to graph your data. In your graph you must include the temperature measurements of the water before the ammonium nitrate was added.

3. Calculate the change in temperature, $\Delta T = T_{final} - T_{initial}$.

4. Calculate the heat of solution, q. Assume the solution has a density of 1.00 g/mL and a specific heat of 4.184 $JK^{-1}g^{-1}$.

$$q = - (C_{cal}\Delta T + m_{solution}C_s\Delta T)$$

5. Calculate the molar heat of solution, $\Delta H_{solution}$.

$$\Delta H_{solution} = \frac{q}{moles\ of\ NH_4NO_3}$$

6. Calculate ΔH of reaction from the thermodynamic data given as follows.

$$NH_4NO_3\ (s) \rightarrow NH_4^+\ (aq) + NO_3^-\ (aq)$$

ΔH_f° (kJ/mol)	−365.6	−132	−205

How does the calculated value of ΔH compare with your experimental value?

	NH₄NO₃ (s) + H₂O (l)
Net Ionic Reaction	
ΔT	
q	
Experimental $\Delta H_{solution}$	
Calculated $\Delta H_{solution}$	

Part 4. The Heat of Neutralization

1. Using a graduated cylinder, add 50.0 mL of 3.0 M NaOH to the calorimeter. Cover it with the lid and let the NaOH solution sit for 4 minutes. Record the temperature.

2. Measure 50.0 mL of 3.0 M HCl in a clean graduated cylinder. Record the temperature. The temperature of the HCl and NaOH solutions should be the same (within 0.2°C). If the temperatures are not the same, adjust the temperature of the HCl by running warm or cold tap water on the outside of the graduated cylinder.

3. Quickly but carefully add the HCl to the calorimeter. Put the lid on. Stir the solution and record the temperature every 15 seconds for 4 minutes.

4. Pour the waste into the appropriately labeled waste container in the hood. Clean and dry the calorimeter.

5. Repeat the measurement (steps 1-5) using acetic acid, 3 M CH_3COOH, instead of HCl.

Calculate the Heat of Neutralization

1. Write the balanced net ionic equation for HCl reacting with NaOH. HCl is a strong acid and NaOH is a strong base. Both dissociate completely in aqueous solution.

2. Graph the data and determine T_M. In your graph you must include the temperature measurements of the 50 mL NaOH in the calorimeter before the HCl was added.

3. Calculate the change in temperature of the solution and the heat of neutralization, q.

$$\Delta T = T_{final} - T_{initial} = T_M - T_{initial}$$
$$q = -(C_{cal}\Delta T + m_{solution}C_s\Delta T)$$

In this equation, $m_{solution}$ is the mass of the solution (total volume): 50 mL 3 M HCl plus 50 mL 3 M NaOH. Assume all solutions have a density of 1.00 g/mL and a specific heat of 4.184 J $K^{-1}g^{-1}$.

4. Calculate the molar heat of neutralization, $\Delta H_{neutralization}$.

$$\Delta H_{neutralization} = \frac{q}{\text{moles of } H_2O \text{ produced}}$$

The molar heat of neutralization is the heat released per mole of H_2O produced in the reaction. To calculate the number of moles of H_2O produced, the limiting reagent must be determined.

$$H^+ + OH^- \rightarrow H_2O$$

5. Calculate the molar heat of neutralization for CH_3COOH reacting with NaOH.

    CH_3COOH is a weak acid and does not like to give up a proton, H^+, in aqueous solution. However, the OH^- is a strong base and will take the $H+$ from CH_3COOH until the reaction has gone to completion. The net ionic reaction for CH_3COOH reacting with NaOH is as follows.

    $$CH_3COOH + OH^- \rightarrow CH_3COO^- + H_2O$$

6. Calculate ΔH for each of the following reactions from the thermodynamic data given.

    $$H^+ (aq) + OH^- (aq) \rightarrow H_2O (l)$$
    ΔH_f° (kJ/mol)   0   −230.0   −285.83

    $$CH_3COOH (aq) + OH^- (aq) \rightarrow CH_3COO^- (aq) + H_2O(l)$$
    ΔH_f° (kJ/mol)   −485.76   −230.0   −486.01   −285.83

    How do the calculated values of ΔH compare with your experimental values?

	HCl + NaOH	CH₃COOH + NaOH
Net Ionic Reaction		
ΔT		
q		
Experimental $\Delta H_{neutralization}$		
Calculated $\Delta H_{neutralization}$		

PRE-LAB QUESTIONS

1. Define specific heat capacity. Why is the specific heat capacity of water unusually high?

2. How much heat is required to raise the temperature of 50.0 g of water from 35°C to 55°C? Be sure to include units.

3. If 50.0 mL of 10.0°C water is added to 40.0 mL of 65.0°C, calculate the final temperature of the mixture assuming no heat is lost to the surroundings, including the container. Is your answer reasonable?

4. In Part 1 of this experiment, you will determine the heat capacity of the calorimeter. The styrofoam cup calorimeter is shown Figure 1. A typical heat capacity of this type of calorimeter is between 20 and 50 J/K.
    a) What is the heat capacity of the calorimeter due to?
    b) Why do we use two Styrofoam cups?
    c) After the hot water is mixed with the cold water, why should the lid be placed on the cup when the temperature measurements are made? Will the heat capacity of the calorimeter be higher of lower with the lid off?
    d) Some students who stirred too vigorously ended up with a negative heat capacity for their calorimeter. These students continued to do the experiment and determined the heat capacity of a metal and heats of reaction, using the negative heat capacity for the calorimeter. Explain why a negative heat capacity was obtained and if the results for the remainder of the experiment could possibly be reasonable.

    NOTE: Please RETURN the thermometers, lids and Styrofoam cups but discard lids with rips or holes in it. The stockroom has more lids and cups if needed.

5. In a calorimeter, 50.0 mL of 60.0°C water is added to 50 mL of 14.0°C water. If the maximum temperature, T_M, was determined to be 36.0°C, calculate the heat capacity of the calorimeter, C_{cal}.

6. In Part 2 of this experiment you will measure the heat capacity for a metal. The metal must be thoroughly dry. The metal is inside a test tube and the test tube is placed in a hot water bath for 20 minutes to heat the metal. Why do you need to wait 20 minutes? How does the metal get to the temperature of the water bath? In other words, how is the heat transferred from the water to the metal on a molecular level?

7. In Part 3 of this experiment, you will measure the heat of reaction for the dissolution of NH_4NO_3 (s).

    $$NH_4NO_3 \text{ (s)} \quad \rightarrow \quad NH_4^+ \text{ (aq)} + NO_3^- \text{ (aq)}$$

    Some dissolution reactions are endothermic and some are exothermic. W here does the heat come from?

8. In Part 4 of this experiment, you will measure the heat of neutralization reactions.
    a) Write the net ionic equation for HCl reacting with NaOH.
    b) Write the net ionic equation for CH_3COOH reacting with NaOH.
    c) For neutralization reactions, where does the heat come from?

DISCUSSION QUESTIONS

Are you confident in the identification of your unknown metal? How does the atomic mass of the metal calculated using the Law of Dulong and Petit compare with the actual atomic mass? What are the greatest sources of error in this experiment? Is the dissolution of NH_4NO_3 exothermic or endothermic? How does the calculated value of ΔH compare to your experimental value of ΔH for the dissolution of NH_4NO_3? Is the acid-base neutralization reaction exothermic or endothermic? How do the calculated values of $\Delta H_{neutralization}$ compare to your experimental values of $\Delta H_{neutralization}$? Explain why your values may be high or low and discuss possible sources of error?

QUESTIONS

1. In this experiment, how would the value of the atomic mass of the metal calculated be affected if the hot metal sample cooled off before it was transferred to the water in the calorimeter? Would it be too high or too low? Explain your answer.

2. In this experiment, if the hot metal sample was wet, before it was transferred to the water in the calorimeter, how would this effect the experimental heat capacity of the metal? Explain your answer in terms of the specific heat of water relative to that of the metal you used in this experiment.

3. A 10.0 g piece of metal at 100°C is transferred to a calorimeter containing 50.0 mL of water initially at 23.0°C. Calculate the specific heat capacity of the metal if the heat capacity of the calorimeter, C_{cal}, is 25.0 J/K. The final temperature, T_{final}, is 25.6°C.

4. The heat of combustion for a sample of coal is 23.0 kJ/g. What quantity of coal (in grams) must be burned to heat 500.0 g of water from 20.0°C to 95.0°C. The specific heat capacity of water is 4.184 $J°C^{-1}g^{-1}$. Is your answer reasonable?

5. The combustion of carbon monoxide is exothermic.

$$CO\ (g)\ +\ ^1/_2\ O_2\ (g)\ \rightarrow\ CO_2\ (g) \qquad \Delta H\ =\ -283.0\ kJ$$

Determine ΔH for each of the following reactions.

a) $2\ CO\ (g)\ +\ O_2\ (g)\ \rightarrow\ 2\ CO_2\ (g)$

b) $2\ CO_2\ (g)\ \rightarrow\ 2\ CO\ (g)\ +\ O_2\ (g)$

6. Consider the following reaction.

$$H_2\ (g)\ +\ 2\ CO\ (g)\ \rightarrow\ H_2O_2\ (l)\ +\ 2\ C\ (s) \qquad \Delta H\ =\ +33.3\ kJ$$

Calculate the enthalpy change when 5 mole of CO is consumed.

■ EXPERIMENT 6

A Titration for the Determination of Ions in Water: The Hard Truth

Kristen Spotz

OBJECTIVES

- Determine the ions responsible for hard water.
- Determine the relative hardness of tap water by titration.
- Explore commercial methods for water softening.
- Develop the laboratory skills required for accurate and precise quantitative measurements.

INTRODUCTION

You are strolling the aisles of the grocery store in search of the hand soaps when you spot two bar soaps, one specifically designed for hard water and the other for soft water. Would you know which brand to buy?

You receive your electric bill and it is significantly higher than normal. Your neighbor suggests investigating the hardness of your water. Would you understand the possible connection?

On the news you hear conflicting health reports concerning the benefits of having hard versus soft water. What would you do? Your first step to being a more informed consumer involves becoming more aware of what exactly is in your water that causes the condition known as water hardness.

BACKGROUND

Water and Water Hardness

The water we drink and use to cook, bathe and do our laundry is hardly pure. In fact tap water contains many "surprises", one of which is dissolved ions. In particular, two metal ions, which you will determine in this experiment, are largely responsible for the condition known as water hardness. One problem with hard water occurs when the hard water ions bind to soap to form insoluble precipitates which reduce the effectiveness of the soap. These solid precipitates cause soap scum or "bath tub ring" and wind up floating in water and later settling to form a sticky, gummy substance on the bottom of sinks, tubs, showers, and other water-using appliances.

Another problem with hard water occurs when hard water ions are heated causing a solid rocklike deposit of calcite crystals to form. These calcite crystals eventually cause a build-up of "scale" within plumbing as shown in the cross section of the pipe in Figure 1. Scale decreases the overall efficiency of water using appliances and leads to greater fuel consumption and higher utility bills. Hard water clogs your pipes, prevents soaps from sudsing and lowers the efficiency and the life-span of water-using appliances. An analysis of hard water gives an indication about the overall quality of the water supply.

Figure 1: Cross-section of a pipe clogged with scale

Analyzing Hard Water

In this experiment, the degree of hardness will be determined using an analytical method known as a titration. The titration will be performed using ethylenediaminetetraacetic acid, EDTA. EDTA is a weak polyprotic acid and can lose four hydrogens at high pH (basic solution) resulting in the ethylenediaminetetraacetate anion (Figure 2).

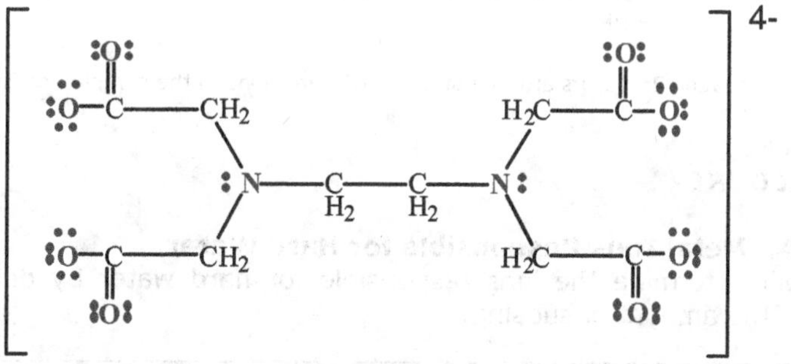

Figure 2: The ethylenediaminetetraacetate anion

In the EDTA molecule, four of the oxygen atoms, along with the two nitrogen atoms, can each grab onto a metal cation by donating their lone pair of electrons. Therefore, the EDTA molecule binds to a single metal cation in up to six places (like the fingers of your hand wrapping around a ball), which makes the resulting complex very strong. When EDTA is introduced into a given sample of water, the EDTA complexes with various cations, including any present hard water ions, in a 1:1 mole ratio (Equation 1 and Figure 3).

$$X^{n+} (aq) + EDTA^{4-} (aq) \rightarrow X(EDTA)^{(4-n)} (aq)$$

Equation 1: X^{n+} represents the hard water ions and $X(EDTA)^{(4-n)}$ represents the "complex ion".

We can determine the quantity of hard-water ions in solution by adding EDTA drop-wise until we have added enough to form a 1:1 complex with all the hard water ions in solution. If we keep track of how much EDTA we add, we can make a conclusion about the amount of hard water ions that must be present. This point, where we have added just enough EDTA, is called the endpoint or equivalence point of the titration. The equivalence point is defined as the quantity of titrant (the substance added) necessary to complex with the analyte (the substance being analyzed). The problem is how do we know when we have reached the endpoint and have added just enough EDTA?

In order to detect the endpoint in this particular titration we will use the indicator, Eriochrome black T, along with a source of magnesium ions, $MgCl_2$. The magnesium is needed because the indicator, which is normally **blue** will form a **pink**

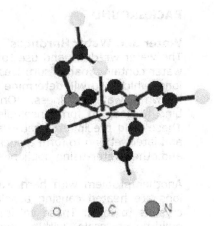

Figure 3: A three-dimensional model of the EDTA complex. The white circle in the center represents the hard water ion.

complex in the presence of magnesium ions. As we begin our titration, the sample is **pink** due to the presence of indicator and magnesium ions (everything else in the solution, including the hard water ions, is colorless). As EDTA is introduced into the water sample, the hard water ions bind to the EDTA molecule in a 1:1 mole ratio. Once the EDTA is bound to all the hard water ions, the EDTA begins to pull the magnesium ions away from the indicator, In (Equation 2). The endpoint is noted when the solution turns **blue** due to the lack of magnesium ions that are available to bind with the indicator.

$$\textbf{MgIn (aq)} + \text{EDTA}^{4-} \text{ (aq)} \rightarrow \text{Mg(EDTA)}^{2-} \text{ (aq)} + \textbf{In}^{2-} \textbf{ (aq)}$$
Pink   Blue

Equation 2: Occurs after all of the hard water ions in the sample are first complexed with EDTA.

PROCEDURE

Part A: Metal Ions Responsible for Hard Water
You will determine the ions responsible for hard water by determining which metal ions reduce the amount of sudsing.

Chemicals Used	Materials Used
Magnesium nitrate	Test tubes (5)
Sodium nitrate	Rubber stoppers (5)
Calcium nitrate	Metal spatula
Potassium nitrate	Test tube rack
De-ionized water	Analytical balance
Liquid Ivory™ soap	Disposable dropper

1. Label the test tubes 1-5. Each of the first four test tubes will contain about 0.5 grams of one of the following compounds: sodium nitrate, calcium nitrate, magnesium nitrate, or potassium nitrate. Record the contents of each test tube.

2. Half-fill each of the five test tubes with de-ionized water. Test tube #5 has only de-ionized water and will serve as a control. Stopper each test tube and shake until each solute is dissolved.

3. Add three drops of Ivory™ soap to each test tube. Shake vigorously for 5 seconds and allow the contents to settle. Sketch your observations of the level of sudsing for each test tube. Dispose of all solutions down the sink.

Part B: Titration of Hard Water

You will perform titrations to determine the hardness of a sample of local water. You will begin your analysis by titrating a blank.

Chemicals Used	Materials Used
EDTA stock solution	Ring stand and buret clamp
Buffer solution (pH 10)	250-mL Erlenmeyer flasks (4)
Indicator (Eriochrome black T)	10-mL Graduated cylinders
Magnesium chloride solution	100-mL, 250-mL Beakers
De-ionized water	50-mL Buret
Various water samples	Funnel
	Hot plate
	1-mL, 50-mL Volumetric pipets and pipet bulb

CAUTION: Be careful, hot plates can stay warm for a long time after they are turned off.

1. Prepare a sample of tap water for study by first allowing the water to run about two minutes to flush the pipes. Take about 250 mL of the tap water and set aside for study as described below.

2. Prepare a 50-mL buret. Begin by running about 50 mL of de-ionized water through the buret and then rinse the buret with about 5.0 mL of EDTA solution. Use a 100-mL beaker to collect the waste.

3. Mount the buret in the ring stand and, using a funnel, fill the buret with stock solution of EDTA. Record the concentration of EDTA solution and the initial buret volume.

4. Prepare the blank solution to be titrated. Begin by pipeting 50.00 mL of de-ionized water into a 250-mL Erlenmeyer flask. Record the color after each of the following additions (placing a piece of white paper under the flask will help you accurately see the color). Add 5.00 mL of buffer and 2-3 drops of the indicator, Eriochrome black T. Pipet 1.0 mL of the $MgCl_2$ solution to the blank while swirling the flask. Heat the solution to 50-60°C. Remove the flash from the hot plate. The warm solution is now ready to titrate.

5. Titrate the solution in the flask with EDTA. The endpoint comes very soon with the blank titration so adjust the buret to dispense the EDTA drop-wise. Swirl the flask to mix the solution during the titration. The solution should turn from dark pink to dark purple to dark blue. When the last tinge of purple disappears, stop and allow the solution to sit for a few moments because the indicator is slow to react. Set this solution aside and save as a reference endpoint for the other titrations. Record the volume of EDTA (± 0.02 mL) needed to titrate the blank. This volume will be subtracted out in following titrations to account for the amount of magnesium ions added.

6. Prepare a sample of tap water for titrating. Follow the directions used in step 4 above, but substitute 50.00 mL of tap water for the 50.00 mL of de-ionized water used previously.

7. Refill the buret with EDTA, record the initial volume and titrate the solution of tap water following the directions in step 5 above. The endpoint will take longer to reach than with the blank.

8. Repeat steps 6 and 7 until you have two trials with volumes of EDTA (corrected for the blank) within 2% of each other. Error is calculated using the following formula:

$$\text{Error} = \left(\frac{\text{Trial I - Trial II}}{\text{Trial I}} \right) \times 100 \leq 2\%$$

9. All waste can be poured down the sink with copious amounts of water.

Part C: Water Softening
You will evaluate the effectiveness of a commercial water softener (Calgon™).

Chemicals Used	Materials Used
Calgon™	Well plate with 24 wells
Tap water and de-ionized water	Plastic pipets and Glass stir rods

Instructions
1. Using a 24-well plate, half-fill wells A1 and A2 with de-ionized water and half-fill wells A3 and A4 with tap water. Add one drop of Calgon™ to wells A2 and A4 and stir.

2. To all of the wells (A1 - A4), add one drop of buffer and one drop of indicator. Note and record the color changes. All waste can be poured down the sink.

A Titration for the Determination of Ions in Water: The Hard Truth

Name:	Lab Instructor:
Date:	Lab Section:

PRE-LABORATORY EXERCISES

1. Read the section on titration in your textbook. In your own words, rewrite a brief description of what is involved in a titration.

2. Do you expect that de-ionized water would be hard or soft? Why?

3. Thanks to King Henry VIII, a common way of reporting water hardness is in grains per gallon where 1 grain=64.0 mg. If natural water averages a relative hardness of 6.00 grains per gallon convert this to mg/liter.

4. One way of combating hard water is to use soaps and detergents with added phosphates. Phosphates bind with the hard water ions to form insoluble precipitates, instead of the ions binding with the soap. Make a list, using the solubility rules in your text, of 6 insoluble ionic compounds that contain the phosphate ion.

OVER →

PRE-LABORATORY EXERCISES continued...

5. Explain the purpose of everything you added to make your blank in Part B, step 4. What is the purpose of titrating the blank?

A Titration for the Determination of Ions in Water: The Hard Truth

Name:	Lab Instructor:
Date:	Lab Section:

RESULTS and POST-LABORATORY QUESTIONS

Part A: Metal Ions Responsible for Hard Water

Indicate the ion present and sketch the relative level of water and suds for each test tube.

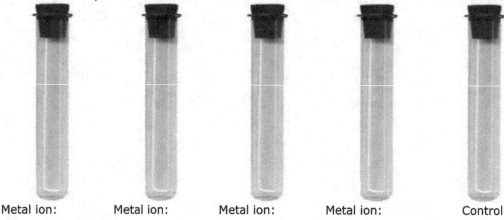

| Metal ion: | Metal ion: | Metal ion: | Metal ion: | Control |

Based on the sudsing test in Part A, which two metal ions are likely responsible for water hardness? Explain.

Part B: Titration of Hard Water

Volume of EDTA used to titrate blank

	Trial #1	Trial #2	Trial #3	Trial #4
Tap water:				
Initial buret reading				
Final buret reading				
Total volume of EDTA				
Vol. corrected for blank				

Put a star (*) next to the two trials that are within 2%.

Average corrected vol. of EDTA (use selected trials, *)
Concentration of EDTA (from stock bottle)
Number of moles of EDTA needed to titrate sample
Number of moles of hard water ions present in sample
Volume of hard water sample analyzed
Concentration (mol/L) of hard water ions in water sample
Class average: Concentration of hard water ions

OVER →

RESULTS and POST-LABORATORY QUESTIONS continued...

Part B: Titration of Hard Water continued

1. What color was the blank solution after you added 5 mL of buffer and seven drops of indicator? What species were causing the color?

    What color appeared after the magnesium chloride was added? What species were causing the color?

    What color appeared after titrating with EDTA? What species were causing the color?

2. Research indicates that students who write about and talk about science in informal settings often exhibit a deeper level of content mastery. With this in mind, we ask you to write a hypothetical letter to a friend or relative explaining hard/soft water along with the consequences and drawbacks of hard water. Based on your knowledge of hard/soft water, would you recommend they soften their water and why? Include specific information about the actual hardness of your water (see the table below). You can be specific about what water in your house you would choose to soften. In addition, explain a sample test that they can perform to determine if their water is hard. When writing your letter, it is important to know that there are conflicting reports concerning hard/soft water. For example, softening water (removing the hard water ions) increases your risk of heart disease because sodium ions are "exchanged" for the hard water ions in the process. The U.S. Department of Agriculture's Human Nutrition Research Center has stated, "The health benefits of drinking hard water far outweigh the minor inconveniences." However, having hard water increases children's and infants' risk of developing eczema, a skin condition characterized by an itchy rash. This may be due to the increased amount of soap needed in hard water or to the actual minerals in the water.

Hardness Description	Hardness (mol/L)
Soft	$0 - 6.0 \times 10^{-4}$
Moderately Hard	$6.0 \times 10^{-4} - 1.2 \times 10^{-3}$
Hard	$1.2 \times 10^{-3} - 1.8 \times 10^{-3}$
Very Hard	$> 1.8 \times 10^{-3}$

A Titration for the Determination of Ions in Water: The Hard Truth

Name:	Lab Instructor:
Date:	Lab Section:

RESULTS and POST-LABORATORY QUESTIONS continued...

Part C: The Effect of Commercial Water Softeners on Hard Water

Well	Contents	Color (after indicator and buffer)
A1		
A2		
A3		
A4		

Explain the significance of each of the four wells. Why was each well necessary to see if the water softener was working?

Did the commercial water softener appear to help soften the water? Explain.